COLLECTIBLE MOVIE POSTERS

ILLUSTRATED GUIDE WITH AUCTION PRICES

JIM HALPERIN AND HECTOR CANTU, EDITORS

FOREWORD BY SARA KARLOFF

Whitman
Publishing, LLC
PUBLISHING SINCE 1934
www.whitman**books**.com

COLLECTIBLE MOVIE POSTERS
ILLUSTRATED GUIDE WITH AUCTION PRICES

Publishing, LLC
PUBLISHING SINCE 1934
www.whitman**books**.com

© 2010 WHITMAN PUBLISHING, LLC
3101 CLAIRMONT ROAD • SUITE C • ATLANTA, GEORGIA 30329

Correspondence concerning this book may be directed to the publisher, attn: Collectible Movie Posters, at the address above.

ISBN: 0794831427
Printed in China

Caveat: The values indicated are subject to variation. Before making decisions to buy or sell, consult the latest information. Grading of collectible movie posters is subject to interpretation, and opinions can vary. Any value estimate or past auction price may have little relevance to future transactions. Such factors as changing demand, popularity, new discoveries, strength of the overall market, and economic conditions are influences.

Advertisements within this book: Whitman Publishing, LLC, does not endorse, warrant, or guarantee any of the products or services of its advertisers. All warranties and guarantees are the sole responsibility of the advertiser.

About the cover: Five of the most striking of the 100 posters showcased in this book are, from left to right, *The Mad Doctor* (ranked no. 7), *Flying Down to Rio* (no. 4), *The Bride of Frankenstein* (no. 1), *Son of Kong* (no. 16), and *Snow White and the Seven Dwarfs* (no. 19).

If you enjoy *Collectible Movie Posters,* you will also enjoy Whitman Publishing's line of VAULT books on sports, politics, World War II, famous entertainers, and other subjects. Each VAULT book holds a treasure trove of collectible memorabilia replicas that can be removed and examined alongside the text and photographs.

For a complete catalog of numismatic reference books, supplies, and storage products, visit Whitman Publishing online at www.whitmanbooks.com.

CONTENTS

ABOUT THE EDITORS

Jim Halperin is cofounder of Heritage Auction Galleries, which with approximately $700 million in annual sales is the world's largest numismatic company as well as the third-largest auction house in America. He is an active collector of EC comics, movie posters, and early 20th-century American art, as well as a venture capital investor, philanthropist, and part-time novelist. His first novel, *The Truth Machine,* was published in 1996 and became an international science fiction bestseller. It was optioned for movie development by Warner Bros. and Lions Gate. Jim's second novel, *The First Immortal,* was published in 1998 and immediately optioned as a Hallmark Hall of Fame television miniseries. Jim's collection can be viewed at www.jhalpe.com.

Hector Cantu is editorial director at Heritage Auction Galleries, where he produces its official publication, *Heritage Magazine.* In addition to being a movie fan and collector, he is the cocreator of the nationally syndicated newspaper comic strip *Baldo.*

FOREWORD

By Sara Karloff

**Boris Karloff with daughter Sara.
Photo courtesy of the Karloff estate.**

Goodness, how I wish my father had kept some of his movie posters!

But dad was not a collector. He brought home scripts for the movies, television shows, and stage plays he was working on. But props? Costumes? Movie posters? I don't think he thought twice about those things. No one did in those days! Most of it was thrown out. Which is probably what makes a collectible a collectible.

It's amazing. Every day I marvel at the number of people my father touched, whether they were movie fans or Hollywood stars. My father, Boris Karloff, was a warm and lovely human being, respected by those he worked with and adored by those who knew him personally. The perpetuation of that legacy is due in main part to his fans. When I travel, it's a lovely experience to have people thank me for my father's work. These are the people who keep his memory alive. It's rather interesting that a man known for his warmth and compassion achieved fame by playing a monster. He did such a fantastic job, I'm proud to say, that few actors in the history of horror are so closely identified with the genre as my father. In that respect, he shares the stage with stars such as Bela Lugosi, who brought life to Count Dracula, and Lon Chaney, who so wonderfully played the Phantom of the Opera.

And don't forget Ginger Rogers and Fred Astaire, Errol Flynn, Barbara Stanwyck, Douglas Fairbanks, Peter Lorre, and Greta Garbo. These great stars also epitomized their own genres and touched millions of people in their own unique ways.

Unfortunately, most of what's left from Hollywood's early years, aside from the movies themselves, are the posters the studios printed to promote these stars and their films. I'm still startled when I see my father's made-up face peering from the one sheet for *The Bride of Frankenstein* or his green eyes staring at me from a *Black Cat* half sheet. Movie poster artwork is incredibly striking and iconic, and is a big reason why demand has surged in recent years.

Collectible Movie Posters assembles some of the highest prices realized for movie posters over the past eight years and shows why these pieces of Hollywood history should be treasured—not only for their timeless link to our cinema past, but also for their vibrant beauty.

By all means, I'm the first to say these artifacts belong with fans and collectors. I've been fortunate enough to travel around our country as well as abroad, meeting fans and collectors, and, without exception, I have found that they know far more about the films, the studios, and the minutiae of each film than any family member. Their knowledge and enthusiasm for Hollywood's Golden Age is invaluable and collectible in its own right. It is they who have given the careers of my father and his iconic contemporaries such very long legs.

This wonderful book is a tribute to that Golden Age and to the fans who have preserved its images for us all to enjoy and savor.

What makes a movie poster valuable? If you have this book in your hands, that's probably the top question on your mind, and a short story will help answer it.

In 1978, Anne Stafford went shopping for a birthday gift for her husband, a horror movie fan. "He loved Dracula and Sherlock Holmes and stuff by Roger Corman," Stafford says.

The California mom found herself at an antiques store. She didn't know what she was looking for or what she would find. As she prepared to leave, a stack of movie posters caught her eye. As she flipped through the sheets, one piece stood out. "It was stunning," Stafford recalls. "I knew I had a terrific hit on my hands. It was the perfect gift. There were maybe 10 movie posters on that table, but honestly I don't remember what the others were. I just remember the *Freaks* poster."

Stafford paid $10 for the insert and took it home to her husband, who was delighted with the gift.

When released in 1932, *Freaks* shocked moviegoers. Based on a short story about circus performers, the film by director and producer Tod Browning cast real circus people as "freaks." The creepy factor was too much for audiences, and MGM quickly pulled the movie from distribution, calling it an error in judgment. Promotional items disappeared just as quickly.

Decades later, the movie was a cult classic at revival houses and on college campuses. Interest in original posters—often called "paper" by collectors—skyrocketed, but unfortunately for fans, most of it had been trashed during the movie's hasty retreat from theaters.

Back to the Staffords.

For 30 years, the couple had little idea that the poster hanging on their wall, showing a sideshow midget sitting on the lap of his trapeze-artist wife, was one of the last remaining inserts for the controversial movie. Its uniqueness came to light only when they decided to sell it. One dealer they contacted offered the Staffords $60,000. "I knew it was something special," Anne Stafford says.

She continued her research, discovering that the poster was the only known original insert to ever surface for the film. "Posters from the original release of *Freaks* are virtually unheard of," says Grey Smith, director of vintage movie posters at Heritage Auction Galleries. "They are some of the hobby's greatest rarities."

The couple decided to auction the poster, and in March 2009 it realized $107,550.

Not bad for a $10 investment.

Which brings us to this book.

How This Collection Was Compiled

Over the past 15 years, quality vintage posters for Hollywood's most popular films have shot up in value. In 1994, a movie fan paid $4,600 for a one sheet for the 1936 movie *Love Before Breakfast,* a romantic comedy starring Carole Lombard. In March 2008, the same poster realized $47,800 at a Heritage Auction Galleries auction.

"Before 1990, the most valuable posters were under $10,000," says Smith at Heritage Auction Galleries. "Since then, a growing demand and several significant purchases have made vintage movie posters a hot collectors' market."

In this same period, Heritage Auction Galleries has established itself as the premier source of vintage movie posters, handling approximately 70 percent of worldwide movie poster auction sales annually. Heritage hosts three floor auctions a year, in addition to weekly Internet auctions

Tod Browning's *Freaks* shocked audiences in 1932 and was quickly pulled from theaters.

Between 1994 and 2008, the one sheet for Carole Lombard's 1936 movie *Love Before Breakfast* increased in value by more than 1,000 percent. See page 67 for complete view.

closing every Sunday night. The collection of posters in this book represents 100 of the highest prices realized by Heritage Auction Galleries.

To compile this selection, we examined sales records dating to Heritage's first vintage movie poster auction to find the highest prices realized. In some cases, more than one example of a movie poster appeared on our initial ranking. In these cases, we only list the highest-quality poster sold. For instance, if the initial list included a poster in Very Fine+ condition and another in Very Fine−, we only include the former. If two posters with identical grades made the initial list, our final compilation includes only the most recent sale.

What makes the Staffords' *Freaks* poster a treasure are the same factors that make most of the posters in this book so valuable: extremely low supply coupled with high collector demand. If only one poster for a popular movie is known to exist, expect fierce bidding at auction time. If several exist,

Attack of the 50 Foot Woman may not be popular with critics, but collectors prize posters from the cheesy 1958 science fiction movie.

expect the best-quality specimen to be the most highly prized.

Breaking It Down

Examining our compilation reveals several truths about the most valuable vintage movie posters.

Horror and science fiction are the most popular genres among movie fans, whether it's 1931's *Frankenstein* or 1958's *Attack of the 50 Foot Woman*. Horror masters Boris Karloff and Bela Lugosi claim the most starring roles of the 100 posters, inserts, and lobby cards on this ranking. But don't dismiss the power of The Mouse. Walt Disney's Mickey stars on 12 different posters in this collection.

Among these 100 posters, 13 represent movies released in 1933—the most for any year—including *Flying Down to Rio, The Mad Doctor, King Kong,* and *Duck Soup.* "When the sound era began in the late 1920s, the studios saw that talkies were going to be popular, so all these movies went into production," says Smith, coauthor of *Capes, Crooks & Cliffhangers: Heroic Serial Posters of the Golden Age* (Ivy Press, 2009). "Many people consider these early talkies the classics."

Films released in 1933 also mark a period immediately before Hollywood began enforcing its Production Code, which reined in risqué scenes and story lines. "In the 1933 movie *Baby Face*, Barbara Stanwyck basically played a young woman who sleeps her way to the top," Smith says. "After the Production Code was being enforced, it was

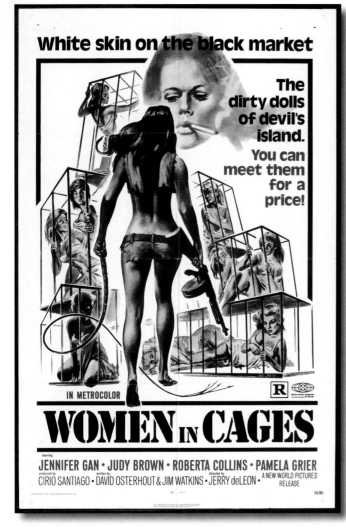

Posters for exploitation or "grindhouse" films such as 1971's *Women in Cages,* coproduced by Roger Corman, are growing in popularity.

hard to find movies like that, or women swimming in the nude, as Jane did in *Tarzan and His Mate.*"

In all, more than 60 of the 100 posters ranked here were released during America's Great Depression. Several factors contribute to the popularity of these pre–World War II posters. "For many collectors, these are the most beautiful posters Hollywood has ever produced," Smith says. "Couple that with the paper drives of World War II, when movie posters were destroyed. On top of that, beginning in the 1950s, fire marshals across the country visited theaters and asked owners to get rid of posters they had stacked in their offices. They were fire hazards. Lots of classic posters were lost."

In this ranking, you'll find no poster printed before 1915 (Charlie Chaplin's *The Champion*) and no poster printed after 1958 (*Attack of the 50 Foot Woman*).

Looking Ahead

For movie poster fans, the 44-year span of movies represented in this book is prime treasure-hunting territory.

But don't rule out posters outside this "classic" category.

Buyers are increasingly pursuing posters printed in Europe after World War II. "Collectors are shifting away from that American mentality. They're beginning to chase posters from the 1940s and 1950s. Some of these are beautiful, especially Italian releases," Smith says, noting the poster for the Italian release of 1947's *The Lady From Shanghai,* which realized nearly $42,000 in March 2008.

Posters for "grindhouse" or exploitation films also are a growing category. "Producers like Sam Arkoff, Jim Nicholson, and Roger Corman would practically design their posters before they made their movies," Smith says. "The films themselves are almost unwatchable, but movie fans love the posters."

But, as with most collectibles, Smith has one piece of buying advice: "Buy what you like and what makes you happy as a movie fan. If there's a movie poster hanging on your wall and you know all about the actors, the director, the crazy behind-the-scenes stories about that film and its production, you are a movie poster collector, no matter how much that poster is worth."

Original Poster Art: A Movie Masterpiece

If anything is rarer than a rare movie poster, it's the original art used for a movie poster.

Original art used for posters was almost never saved. "No one at the studios saw any value in keeping it," says Smith. Most of the work was done anonymously. Artists worked for little money and most weren't even allowed to sign their work, Smith says.

Still, about a quarter of the movie poster art that has survived can be linked to known artists. Among the best-known is Reynold Brown (1917–1991), who completed art for movies like *How the West Was Won, The Alamo, Cat on a Hot Tin Roof, Ben-Hur, Creature From the Black Lagoon,* and *Attack of the 50 Foot Woman.*

Of course, Hollywood sometimes took more high-profile approaches to commissioning artwork.

In 1943, 20th Century–Fox released *The Song of Bernadette,* based on a story written by Franz Werfel after he visited the shrine of the Virgin Mary at Lourdes, France. In the movie, peasant girl Bernadette has a vision of a beautiful lady, which townsfolk believe to be the Virgin Mary. The resulting furor overtakes everyone in the village.

For the movie's posters, 20th Century–Fox hired Norman Rockwell (1894–1978). At the time, the illustrator had completed his famous series of paintings, *The Four Freedoms,* and was riding a wave of worldwide acclaim. In the character of Bernadette as played by actress Jennifer Jones, Rockwell saw a simple girl—"a lone girl, glorious and exalted"—who could inspire people of all walks of life, as stated in the movie's official pressbook.

Rockwell's full-length portrait of Bernadette was the centerpiece of the movie's publicity campaign, and would be among the most popular of Rockwell's career. "Nothing else I have ever painted," Rockwell would say of the work, "was reproduced in so many ways."

The whereabouts of Rockwell's original painting were unknown for a number of years before it was discovered in the private collection of the film's producer, William Perlberg (1900–1968). Ownership subsequently passed to Mount St. Mary's Academy in Los Angeles and then into the hands of a private collector.

While movie posters featuring Rockwell's Bernadette have fetched up to $1,500, his 53" x 28" original oil on canvas realized $478,000 in a November 2005 Heritage Auction Galleries auction.

What's the Condition?

For collectors, the most important factor other than rarity is condition. Serious collectors demand top quality, with the difference between "Fair" and "Mint" often being tens of thousands of dollars.

Mint: A never-used poster. May show minor signs of age and wear at folds due to storage. No holes, no tears.

Near Mint: A generally unused poster with fresh, saturated colors. May have minimal tears at folds. Has no significant holes, no paper loss. May have minor tears along edges, and fine pinholes.

Norman Rockwell's painting for *Song of Bernadette* (left) is among the artist's most popular pieces. Below, the final poster designed around Rockwell's painting.

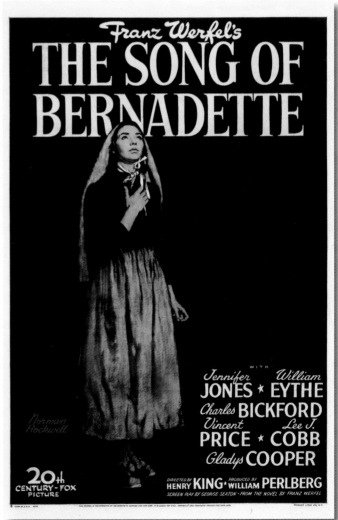

Fine: A poster with bright colors, clean, with general signs of use. May have minor tears at folds with minor paper loss. May have fine pinholes. May have restoration.

Good: An average poster with overall fresh color. May have tears, minor paper loss, minor hazing. Paper may be brittle due to age. May have minor stains or a small amount of writing in an unobtrusive place. May have medium or major restoration.

Fair: A poster with faded colors and brittle paper, showing significant signs of use. May have tears and paper loss, and tape, writing, and stains in image area. In need of restoration or has undergone major restoration.

Poor: A poster that is worn, torn, and damaged. May have staining, cracking, dry rot, and large tears. May be heavily soiled, with pieces missing. In need of major restoration.

Caring For and Storing Your Posters

Your movie poster is a piece of motion-picture history and should be afforded the same care and respect that any historical artifact might be given. The three major destabilizing and destructive elements associated with these paper products are the following:

Direct sunlight: Always keep your posters out of direct sunlight, as ultraviolet (UV) rays can fade inks used in the manufacturing process. When framing a poster, try to use archival or museum mounting elements such as UV-resistant Plexiglas and acid-free mounting boards and mattes.

Moisture: Try to keep your posters from contact with water or moisture such as extreme humidity. Moisture can stain and mildew your poster and deteriorate the elements used in its manufacture.

Heat: Always avoid storing or displaying posters in overly hot environments, as heat and resulting reactions can make paper fibers brittle and "brown" the paper.

In caring for your movie posters, there are various handling and storage techniques that should be used.

Folded posters: For any folded poster, try not to frequently fold and unfold the poster, as this will eventually weaken the paper fibers and cause separation and tearing at the fold lines. For post-1960s glossy stock posters, folding is especially harmful, as inks can flake and fall off along the fold lines with excessive handling. If a poster is rolled or has never been folded, under no

circumstances should it be folded. It is best to store all posters unfolded and flat.

Linen-backed posters: Many collectible posters have been professionally linen backed, a conservation method where the poster is mounted on archival linen. The process can improve appearance, reduce the possibility of deterioration, and increase the poster's value. These posters should be stored flat.

Paper-backed posters: Posters that have been restored by mounting on Japanese or archival paper should be stored flat, as rolling and unrolling can cause fold lines to reappear in the paper.

Framing: When having a poster framed, take the poster to a knowledgeable framer who has experience in acid-free archival museum mounting and framing. Never let a framer heat-mount or adhesive-mount your poster

One sheets such as this one for the original release of *Gone With the Wind* in 1939 are the most common posters printed by movie studios.

For ultimate impact on moviegoers, studios issued wall-size six-sheet posters, like this one for 1952's *Singin' in the Rain*.

One sheet (27" x 41"): These posters were typically printed on thin paper stock and usually displayed in the lobby or outdoors in front of the theater. Studios often printed different styles of posters for the same film, sometimes referred to by letter (as "style A," "style B," and so on). Sometimes, studios issued "teaser" or "advance" posters before a film's release to drum up excitement. This size remained standard until the mid-1980s, when one sheets were slightly shortened to 27" x 40". One sheets produced before 1980 were almost always folded in eighths, with one vertical fold and two horizontal folds. After 1980, they were sent to theaters rolled.

Two sheet (41" x 54"): These are the size of two one sheets placed together along their long sides.

to flatten it. Anything done to frame the poster must always be reversible with no damaging effects. UV-resistant glass is recommended for expensive posters to minimize fading over time.

Poster Sizes

Movie posters were printed in various sizes and shapes from 1910 through 1980. If studio executives were excited about a movie, they would produce a larger number of poster sizes for their film. As with most collectibles, the most valuable posters have few known specimens, typically because an initial press run might have been small, with the movie proving more popular than expected.

From the beginning of the 20th century, the most common size for posters was the one sheet, which is the common size for a lithographer's press bed. Most posters listed in this collection are one sheets and have images only on one side. Most vintage posters have at least one pinhole in each corner, where the paper was tacked up for display.

Three sheet (41" x 81"): Intended to be posted outside of theaters. They were printed in two or three pieces, which had to be aligned at the time of display. For bigger-release films, studios sometimes printed two different styles of three sheets. Studios began producing three sheets in one piece in the early 1970s, and had altogether phased out this size by the early 1980s. These posters were printed in far fewer quantities than one sheets.

Six sheet (81" x 81"): These posters were put together to form a large single image, the size of six one sheets, often featuring artwork altogether different from other posters for the movie. Six sheets were often used outdoors as small billboards. These posters typically had smaller print runs, and, since they were often glued to walls, few survive.

The title lobby card (bottom left) anchors the eight-card set issued for 1956's science fiction classic *Forbidden Planet*.

in this format instead of one sheets from 1935 through 1937. This size gained in popularity in the 1950s as theater owners found them more durable than one sheets.

Smaller Posters

Lobby card (11" x 14"): A set of up to eight small posters usually printed on card stock for theater lobby display. Most lobby cards use photographic images from scenes in the movie. A title lobby card might include all major stars, production credits, and poster artwork. In some cases, lobby card sets have no title lobby card.

Window card (14" x 22"): Produced on heavy cardboard, these small posters were used for advertising away from theaters, typically in shop windows or on telephone poles. They have a 4" blank area at the top of the card for the theater's name and date of showing.

Midget or mini window card (8" x 14"): Printed primarily before 1940, these were smaller versions of window cards, typically with identical artwork. They had the same blank imprint area and were typically used for display at cigar or candy stores and in restaurants. These were printed in much smaller quantities, making them rarer than standard window cards.

Other Posters

Insert (14" x 36"): Printed on card stock, these posters were used in conjunction with one sheets to promote a film. The artwork is usually a mix of photographic and artwork styles, as opposed to the all-artwork one sheets. These cards were often folded in thirds.

Half sheet or display (22" x 28"): Printed on card stock, these were often printed in two styles. One style would be identical to the title lobby card. These posters often combined photography and artwork and were displayed in theater lobbies. They were pictured in studio pressbooks and called "displays," whereas collectors have taken to calling them "half sheets," as they are half the size of a one sheet.

40" x 60": Studios began printing posters slightly larger than two sheets in the early 1930s. They typically were sent to theaters rolled. Many were produced on a thin paper stock by the Hollywood Sign-Makers Union using a silk-screen process with strong, day-glow paints that made for striking graphics. Printers during this time also used a photo-gelatin process. These posters, such as the one for Disney's 1937 *Magician Mickey,* are the rarest for any films from the 1930s. By the 1940s, 40" x 60" posters were being produced on card stock. They disappeared in the early 1980s.

30" x 40": These posters, like the 40" x 60" ones of the 1940s, were printed on card stock and were typically sent to theaters rolled. Disney Studios printed posters

Foreign posters: These vary in size, from 20" x 28.5" for the Japanese release of *Godzilla* to 55" x 78" for the Italian release of *The Lady From Shanghai*.

THE TOP 100 COLLECTIBLE MOVIE POSTERS

Top Horror Movie
Top Sequel
Top One Sheet

The Bride of Frankenstein
Universal, 1935

Starring: Boris Karloff, Colin Clive, Elsa Lanchester
Price: $334,600
Sold: November 2007
Description: One sheet (27" x 41"), style D, Fine+ on linen

A classic movie and a one-of-a-kind poster combine for the ultimate movie-poster treasure. With a skilled mix of dark humor and gothic horror, director James Whale produced a sequel that surpassed the original film based on Mary Shelley's genre-defining novel. Today, *The Bride of Frankenstein* is considered Whale's masterpiece and the greatest of Universal's horror films. All posters associated with the movie were believed documented until this vibrant style D one sheet emerged from a private collection. Until it surfaced, images of this poster had only been seen in the film's official pressbook. See also the posters ranked 17 and 35 (shown below).

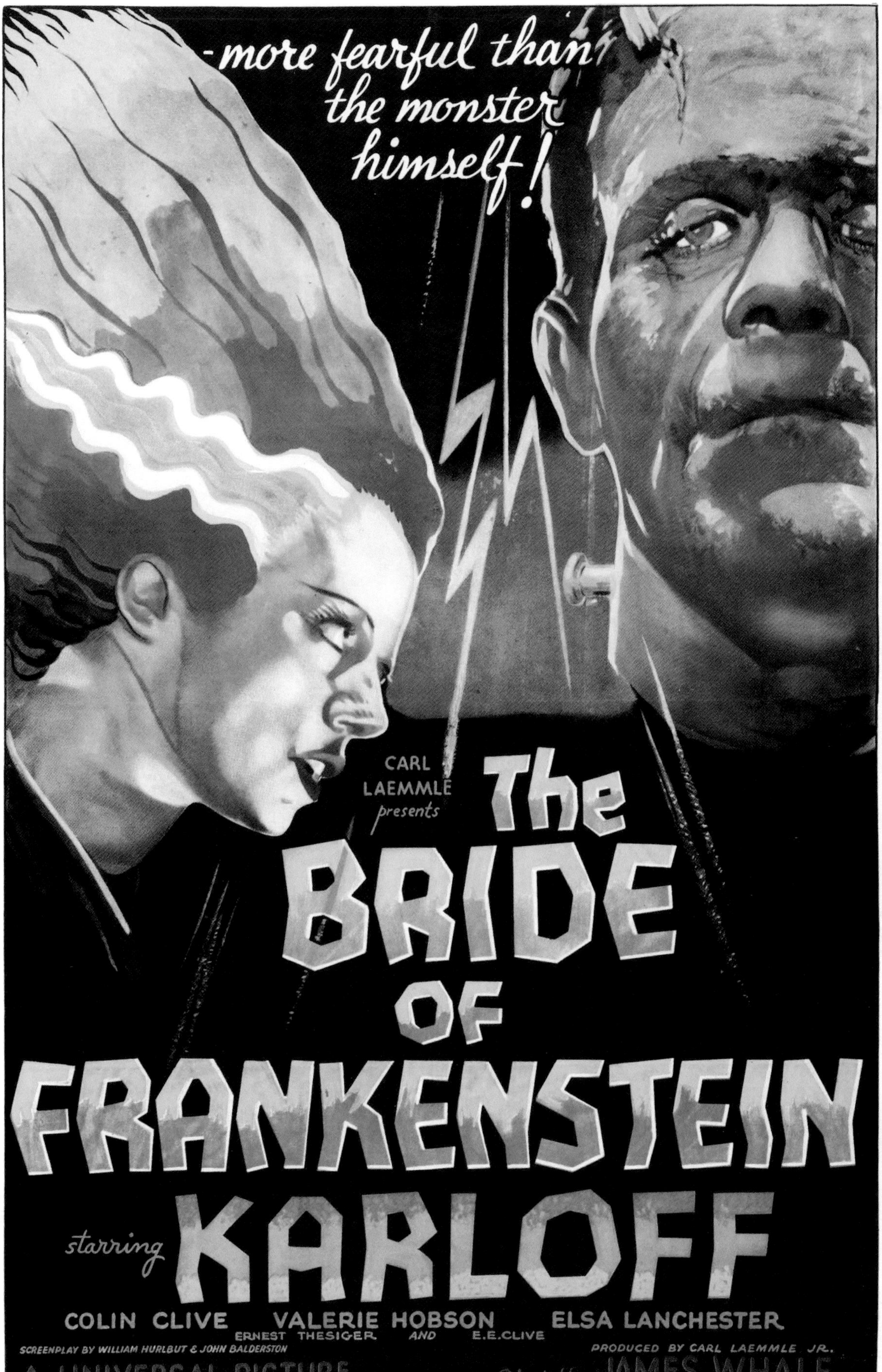

COUNTRY OF ORIGIN U.S.A.

5746

Dracula
Universal, 1931

Starring: Bela Lugosi
Price: $310,700
Sold: March 2009
Description: One sheet (27" x 41"), style F, Very Fine on linen

Before *Frankenstein*, Bela Lugosi created a cultural icon with his portrayal of Bram Stoker's Dracula. Universal Studios produced various one-sheet posters when the supernatural chiller debuted in theaters. One has the tagline "A Nightmare of Horror!" and shows the count grasping a young woman's neck. Another shows large eyes in the darkness peering at a young beauty. This style F one sheet is one of only three known examples. See also the posters ranked 18, 36, and 59 (shown below).

The Black Cat
Universal, 1934

Starring: Boris Karloff, Bela Lugosi
Price: $286,800
Sold: March 2007
Description: One sheet (27" x 41"), Very Fine+ on linen

Horror icons Boris Karloff and Bela Lugosi were cast together for the first time in Edgar G. Ulmer's adaptation of Edgar Allan Poe's classic tale. The film itself is considered a macabre milestone in horror cinema, with its themes of incest, murder, torture, devil worship, and perverse psychological obsessions. Extremely popular with horror fans, original posters from the film are difficult to acquire. Only four specimens of this "beaming-eyed cat" version are known to exist. See also the posters ranked 10 and 38 (shown below).

TOP MUSICAL

Flying Down to Rio
RKO, 1933

Starring: Dolores Del Rio, Ginger Rogers, Fred Astaire
Price: $239,000
Sold: November 2008
Description: One sheet (27" x 41"), Very Fine/Near Mint

Fred Astaire and Ginger Rogers danced the Carioca in this Merian C. Cooper musical production, and a world-famous dance team was born. Needless to say, the film's scantily clad showgirls also helped to make the duo's debut a hit with moviegoers. The poster is one of the rarest in the collecting hobby, with only a handful of the U.S. domestic style known to exist. An international variation is more common, with artwork altered to show less skin on the female figures. See also the posters ranked 79 and 81 (shown below).

Frankenstein
Universal, 1931

Starring: Boris Karloff, Colin Clive
Price: $189,750
Sold: March 2004
Description: One sheet (27" x 41"), Very Fine+ on linen

Considered among the greatest films of all time, director James Whale's *Frankenstein* made a star of Boris Karloff. This poster, one of only five known of this style, includes the first image of the Frankenstein monster with a flat head and neck bolts (earlier teaser posters showed the monster with a fluffy head of hair). The monster would become one of the most recognizable and iconic images of the 20th century. See also the posters ranked 48 and 60 (shown below).

TOP SILENT FILM

The Phantom of the Opera
Universal, 1925

Starring: Lon Chaney, Norman Kerry, Mary Philbin
Price: $155,350
Sold: November 2008
Description: One sheet (27" x 41"), Very Fine– on paper

In 1923, Universal Pictures president Carl Laemmle made cinematic history when he essentially created the horror film with his production of *The Hunchback of Notre Dame*. He returned to the classics two years later with Gaston Leroux's *The Phantom of the Opera*. With Lon Chaney in the starring role, the film was a smash, paving the way for *Dracula, Frankenstein,* and *The Mummy*. At least eight different one-sheet posters were created for the film, with only two depicting the Phantom. Only four specimens of this version are known to exist: one in the Universal Studios archives and three in private collections. See also the poster ranked 93 (shown below).

A UNIVERSAL
PRODUCTION
CARL LAEMMLE
PRESENTS
"THE PHANTOM
OF THE OPERA"
With LON CHANEY
NORMAN KERRY
MARY PHILBIN
AND A CAST OF 5000 OTHERS
STORY BY GASTON LEROUX
DIRECTED BY RUPERT JULIAN
Morgan
"COUNTRY OF ORIGIN, U.S.A."

TOP ANIMATED SHORT

The Mad Doctor
United Artists, 1933

Starring: Mickey Mouse
Price: $107,550
Sold: March 2009
Description: One sheet (27" x 41"), Very Fine/Near Mint

If horror films are popular, a Mickey Mouse horror film is a treasure. *The Mad Doctor* finds Mickey battling an army of skeletons to save Pluto the dog from a Frankenstein-type doctor. This unusually dark seven-minute film was released 14 months after Universal's *Frankenstein*. Beginning in 1932, United Artists produced 13 visually stunning Mickey Mouse one sheets before switching to a stock format in late 1933. These "Magical 13" are among the most sought-after among collectors. Only two examples of this poster are known.

Top Insert

Freaks

MGM, 1932

Starring: Wallace Ford, Leila Hyams
Price: $107,550
Sold: March 2009
Description: Insert (14" x 36"), Fine+

MGM followed Universal's lead into the horror genre with devastating results. Based on a short story by Tod Robbins, *Freaks* lifted the curtain on the garish world of the circus sideshow. Critics and audiences were shocked, and MGM was forced to pull the creepy movie from theaters. Of course, most original posters for the movie also disappeared. Beginning in the early 1960s, *Freaks,* with its popular "one of us" chant, was rediscovered as a counterculture cult film. In the 1970s, what turned out to be the only known insert to survive was purchased from a Southern California antiques store for $10 (see the introduction).

Son of Frankenstein
Universal, 1939

Starring: Basil Rathbone, Boris Karloff, Bela Lugosi
Price: $89,625
Sold: November 2007
Description: Half sheet (22" x 28"), Fine on paper

By the time this movie wrapped, Karloff was in his early 50s and the daily makeup preparation was taking its toll. It would be Karloff's last turn as the Frankenstein monster. *Son of Frankenstein* is the third film in Universal's *Frankenstein* series and the first to feature Lugosi, playing Ygor. Only two specimens of this half sheet are known to exist. See also the poster ranked 71 (shown below).

THE NEW UNIVERSAL PRESENTS

BASIL
RATHBONE
BORIS
KARLOFF
BELA
LUGOSI in

SON of FRANKENSTEIN

with

Lionel ATWILL

JOSEPHINE
HUTCHINSON

DONNIE DUNAGAN

EMMA DUNN · EDGAR NORTON

Produced and directed by Rowland V. Lee

A ROWLAND V. LEE Production

UNIVERSAL

The Black Cat
Universal, 1934

Starring: Boris Karloff, Bela Lugosi
Price: $89,625
Sold: July 2007
Description: Half sheet (22" x 28"), Fine+

The green-eyed faces of Karloff and Lugosi dominate this rarely seen half sheet. Only three are known to exist. Like most half sheets, which were made for theater lobby displays, this poster shows signs of being sent to the movie house in a tube. See also the posters ranked 3 and 38 (shown below).

CARL LAEMMLE presents
KARLOFF AND Bela LUGOSI
SCREENPLAY By PETER RURIC
DIRECTED By EDGAR G. ULMER
PRODUCED By CARL LAEMMLE, JR.
A UNIVERSAL PICTURE
with
DAVID MANNERS
JACQUELINE WELLS
LUCILLE LUND
EGON BRECHER · HARRY CORDING
HENRY ARMETTA · ALBERT CONTI
LOUIS ALBERNI
IN "The BLACK CAT"
BASED ON A STORY BY EDGAR ALLAN POE

Hollywood
Paramount, 1923

Starring: Hope Drown
Price: $89,625
Sold: July 2009
Description: One sheet (27" x 41"), style A, Fine/Very Fine on linen

After the Roscoe "Fatty" Arbuckle and William Taylor scandals, Hollywood was perhaps the most notorious community in America. In other words, it was the perfect setting for a movie. *Hollywood* is the story of a young woman who travels to Los Angeles in search of fame and fortune. What sets this silent movie apart is the chorus of Hollywood villagers in cameo roles, including Mary Astor, Charlie Chaplin, Bebe Daniels, Cecil B. DeMille, Douglas Fairbanks, Alan Hale, Mary Pickford, Will Rogers, and Gloria Swanson. Perhaps most poignantly, Arbuckle—whose career was scuttled in 1921 following the death of actress Virginia Rappe—appears briefly as an unemployed actor, standing in a casting line looking for work.

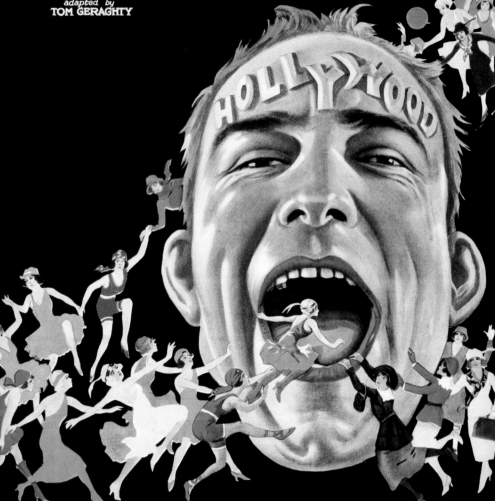

JESSE L. LASKY *Presents a*
JAMES CRUZE
PRODUCTION
HOLLYWOOD

by
FRANK CONDON
adapted by
TOM GERAGHTY

a Paramount Picture

COLLECTIBLE MOVIE POSTERS

TOP WAR MOVIE

Wings

Paramount, 1927

Starring: Clara Bow, Richard Arlen, Buddy Rogers, Gary Cooper
Price: $86,250
Sold: November 2005
Description: One sheet (26" x 40.25"), style D, Very Fine

Director William Wellman's tale of two World War I aviators in love with the same woman was the first winner of the Academy Award® for Best Picture. The movie includes some of the best flying sequences ever captured on film, plus one of the earliest credited appearances of Gary Cooper. This stone lithograph poster is pictured in the movie's original pressbook and is a rare full-bleed poster, which Paramount only produced for its bigger releases. This is the only surviving example. See also the poster ranked 20 (shown below).

King Kong
RKO, 1933

Starring: Fay Wray, Robert Armstrong
Price: $78,200
Sold: March 2002
Description: One sheet (27" x 41"), style A, Very Fine+/Near Mint on linen

When *King Kong* hit theaters, its pioneering special effects and stop-motion models left audiences breathless. In the years since, the image of the giant ape perched atop the Empire State Building with Fay Wray in his fist has become one of the most iconic images in movie history. This one sheet is inspired by the artwork of Kong's stop-motion animator Willis O'Brien, who also worked on *Son of Kong* (1933) and *Mighty Joe Young* (1949). This poster is considered the highest quality of the four known examples. See also the poster ranked 49 (shown below).

TOP WESTERN

Stagecoach
United Artists, 1939

Starring: John Wayne, Claire Trevor
Price: $77,675
Sold: July 2007
Description: One sheet (27" x 41"), Fine/Very Fine on linen

John Ford's western masterpiece about strangers on a stagecoach made John Wayne a star. Today it's considered one of the most influential films ever made, with Orson Welles once saying he studied the movie while making *Citizen Kane. Stagecoach* was nominated for Academy Awards® for Best Picture and Best Director—losing in both cases to *Gone With the Wind.* This stone lithograph poster, which does not depict any of the film's stars (at the time, Wayne was not considered a bankable attraction), is a true rarity.

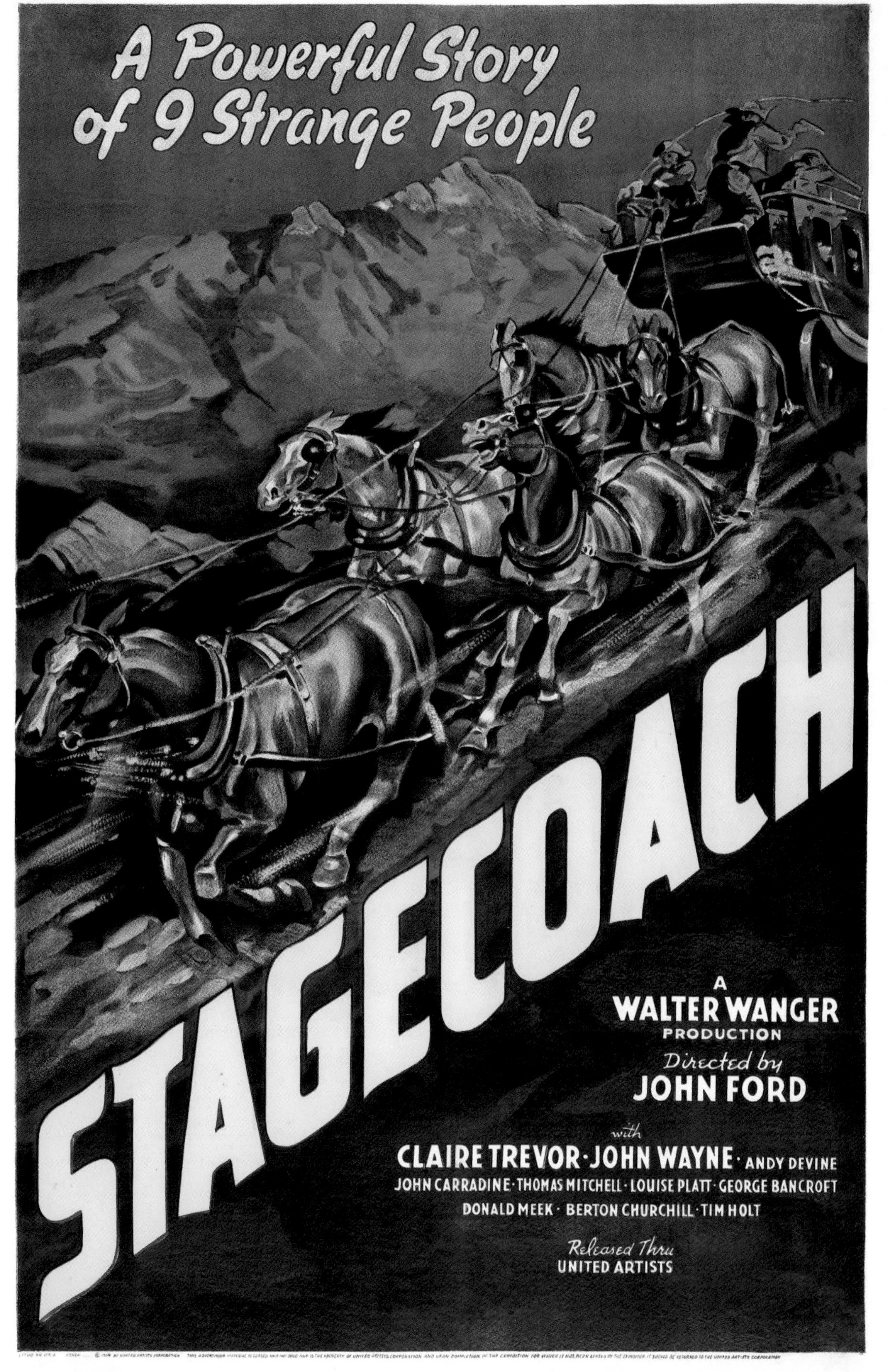

A Powerful Story
of 9 Strange People
STAGECOACH
A
WALTER WANGER
PRODUCTION
Directed by
JOHN FORD
with
CLAIRE TREVOR · JOHN WAYNE · ANDY DEVINE
JOHN CARRADINE · THOMAS MITCHELL · LOUISE PLATT · GEORGE BANCROFT
DONALD MEEK · BERTON CHURCHILL · TIM HOLT
Released Thru
UNITED ARTISTS

Baby Face
Warner Bros., 1933

Starring: Barbara Stanwyck, George Brent
Price: $71,700
Sold: November 2007
Description: One sheet (27" x 41"), Near Mint– on linen

When originally released, this tale of an ambitious young woman (Stanwyck) who uses and abandons men on her way to the top was banned for its explicit sexual content. A heavily edited version was eventually released to theaters (the full uncut version was discovered in 2004). Only five one sheets from the film's original release are known to exist, with this one considered the best.

A WARNER BROS.
& VITAPHONE
PICTURE

Barbara

STANWYCK

and

"BABY
FACE"

WITH
GEORGE BRENT
DIRECTED BY ALFRED E. GREEN

Son of Kong
RKO, 1933

Starring: Robert Armstrong, Helen Mack
Price: $69,000
Sold: July 2006
Description: One sheet (27" x 41"), style B, Very Fine on linen

Son of Kong was produced and released immediately after the success of *King Kong*. The story follows producer Carl Denham's return to Skull Island in search of more monsters. Although the film was not nearly as successful or praised as the original, the popularity of this poster reflects Kong's cultural prominence. Featuring Armstrong and Mack, this stone lithograph is one of the few of its kind, with super-rich color and clean off-white paper.

The Bride of Frankenstein
Universal, 1935

Starring: Boris Karloff, Colin Clive, Elsa Lanchester
Price: $65,725
Sold: July 2007
Description: Half sheet (22" x 28"), Very Good/Fine on paper

Monsters demanding mates seemed especially alluring to audiences of the 1930s. Unlike most one sheets, half sheets typically featured cast photographs. This *Bride of Frankenstein* poster prominently features Karloff and Elsa Lanchester with her shock-white streak of hair. See also the posters ranked 1 and 35 (shown below).

CARL LAEMMLE
Presents
KARLOFF
in
The BRIDE of FRANKENSTEIN
THE MONSTER DEMANDS A MATE!
WITH
COLIN CLIVE
VALERIE HOBSON
ELSA LANCHESTER
UNA O'CONNOR
ERNEST THESIGER
E.E.CLIVE
Produced by
CARL LAEMMLE JR.
Directed by
JAMES WHALE
A UNIVERSAL Picture

TOP TITLE LOBBY CARD

Dracula
Universal, 1931

Starring: Bela Lugosi
Price: $65,725
Sold: November 2007
Description: Title lobby card (11" x 14"), Very Fine+

In addition to the titular vampire, a spider's web and Dracula's "brides" are the main elements in this rare title card. This specimen, with sharp corners and rich colors, is one of the most striking known. See also the posters ranked 2, 36, and 59 (shown below).

Carl Laemmle presents
DRACULA
The VAMPIRE THRILLER
A TOD BROWNING Production
with
BELA LUGOSI
DAVID MANNERS
HELEN CHANDLER
DWIGHT FRYE & Edward Van Sloan
from the famous novel & play by Bram Stoker
produced by Carl Laemmle Jr.
A UNIVERSAL Picture
Made in U.S.A

Top Feature-Length Animated Film

Snow White and the Seven Dwarfs
RKO, 1937

Price: $65,725
Sold: November 2007
Description: Poster (40" x 60"), Very Fine+

This beautiful image featuring the work of animator Grim Natwick and art director Gustav Tenggren practically tells the movie's entire story, with delicate watercolor scenes above a gathering of all the main characters. Despite being labeled "Walt's Folly" during production, the film went on to become the top-grossing film of 1938, and, for a while, the top-grossing film of all time until the 1939 release of *Gone With the Wind*. At 40" x 60", oversized posters were usually intended for front-of-house displays and, due to their large size and fragile paper stock, were rarely saved. The movie's original pressbook shows that this poster was sold to theater owners for $1.25—a substantial amount at the time and possibly the reason so few are known to exist.

His First Full-Length Feature

Walt Disney's

Snow White

and the Seven Dwarfs

Distributed by RKO RADIO PICTURES

in the Marvelous
MULTIPLANE TECHNICOLOR

Wings
Paramount, 1927

Starring: Clara Bow, Richard Arlen, Buddy Rogers, Gary Cooper
Price: $63,250
Sold: July 2005
Description: One sheet (27" x 41"), style C, Very Fine+

When auctioned in 2005, this style C one sheet was the only known example. The movie's original pressbook shows it as one of four styles printed for the first release of the film. This original-release stone lithograph is unrestored. See also the poster ranked 12 (shown below).

Ye Olden Days
United Artists, 1933

Starring: Mickey Mouse
Price: $59,750
Sold: March 2009
Description: One sheet (27" x 41"), Very Fine/Near Mint on paper

---

Before he was officially christened "Goofy," he was Dippy Dawg. He appears as "Ye Prince" in *Ye Olden Days,* an eight-minute short in which Mickey plays a wandering minstrel out to save Minnie from the Prince of Poopoopadoo. This stone lithograph poster is the only known specimen to exist outside of the Disney archives. United Artists' one sheets (1932–1933) are among the highest quality produced for Disney and are considered the rarest of Disney posters.

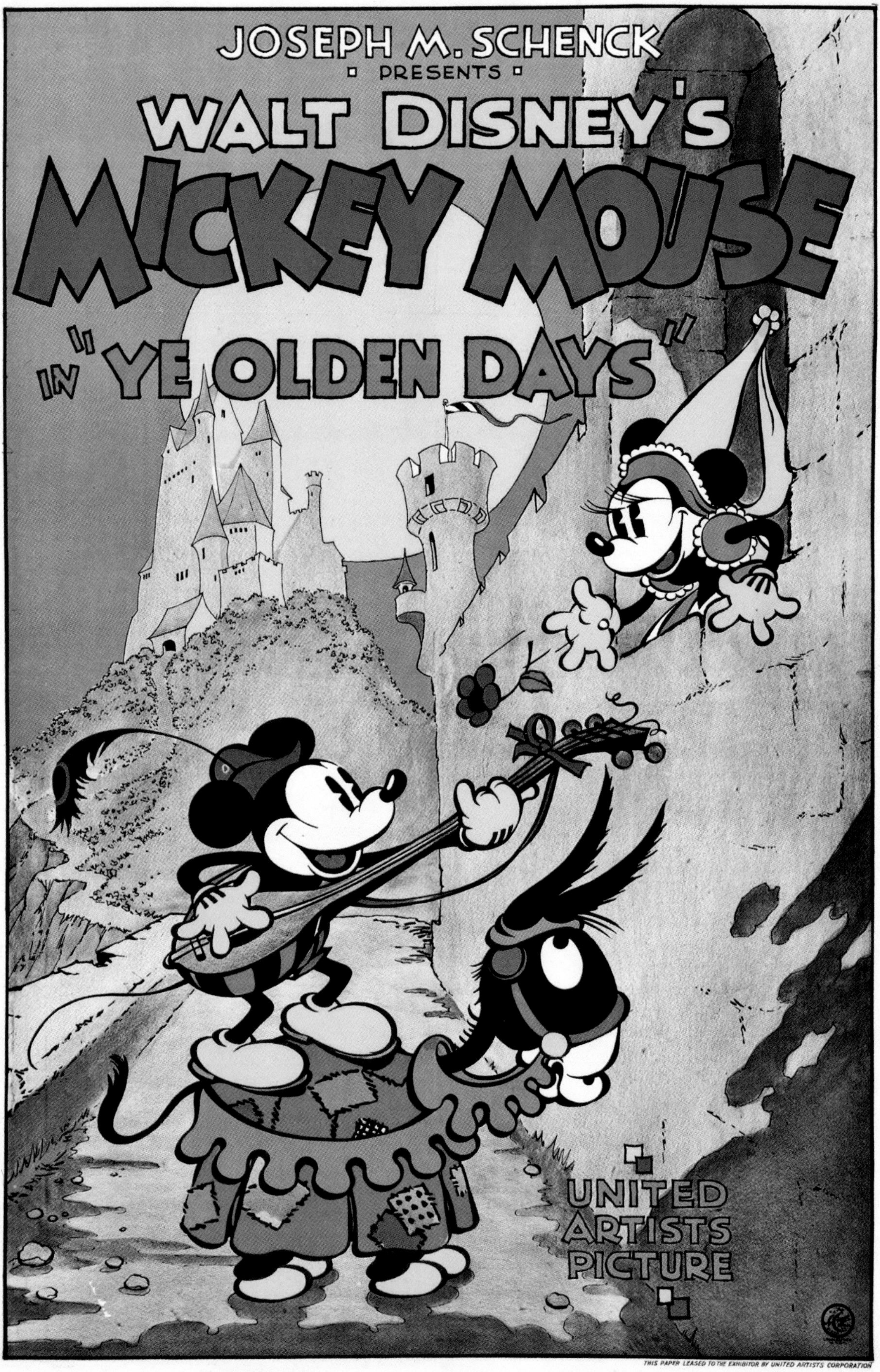

THIS PAPER LEASED TO THE EXHIBITOR BY UNITED ARTISTS CORPORATION

Werewolf of London
Universal, 1935

Starring: Henry Hull, Warner Oland
Price: $59,750
Sold: July 2007
Description: Insert (14" x 36"), Very Fine–

Considered Hollywood's first mainstream werewolf movie, *Werewolf of London* tells the tale of an accursed scientist and his nemesis on the hunt for a cure for their mutual fate. Original posters for this movie are among the rarest of Universal's horror films, with only a handful known to exist.

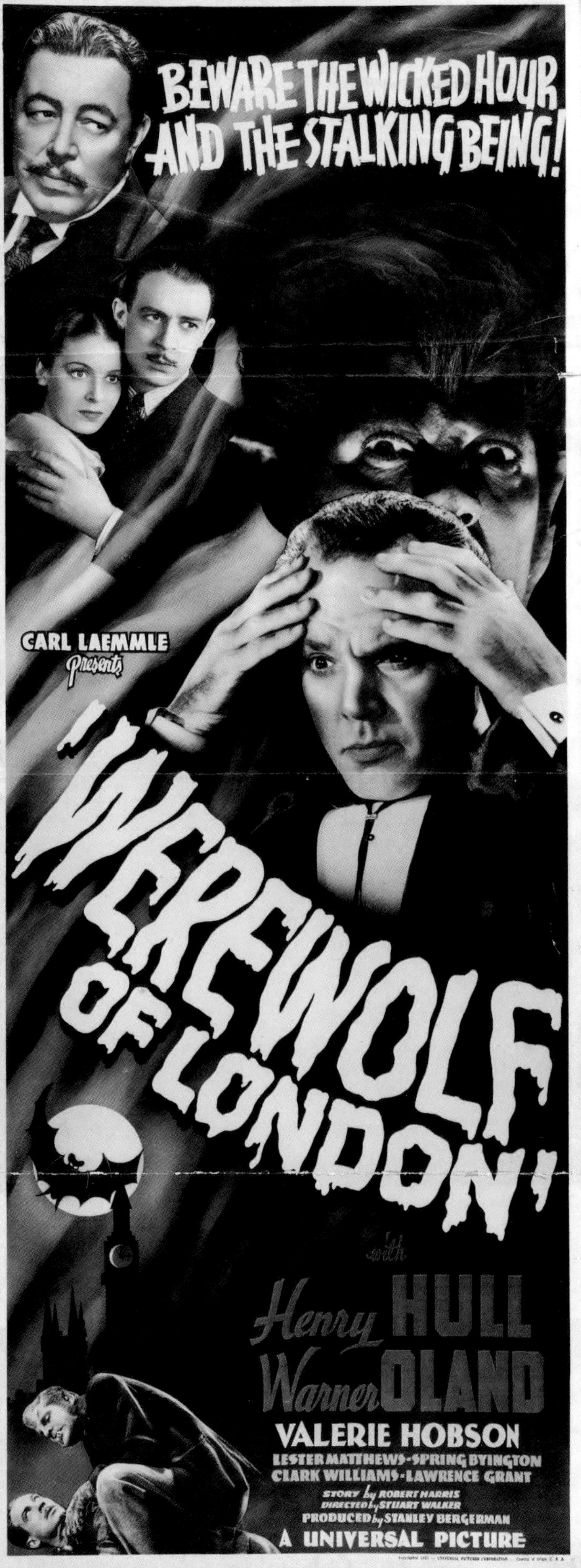
BEWARE THE WICKED HOUR
AND THE STALKING BEING!
CARL LAEMMLE
presents
'WEREWOLF
OF LONDON'
with
Henry HULL
Warner OLAND
VALERIE HOBSON
LESTER MATTHEWS - SPRING BYINGTON
CLARK WILLIAMS - LAWRENCE GRANT
STORY by ROBERT HARRIS
DIRECTED by STUART WALKER
PRODUCED by STANLEY BERGERMAN
A UNIVERSAL PICTURE

The Klondike Kid

United Artists, 1932

Starring: Mickey Mouse
Price: $57,500
Sold: July 2006
Description: One sheet (27" x 41"), Very Fine on linen

Beer mugs, women dancing on tables, and Minnie losing her underpants are all part of this seven-minute pre—Production Code adventure. This poster is among the most desirable for Disney fans, in large part because of the cartoon's Chaplinesque comedy.

JOSEPH M. SCHENCK
PRESENTS
WALT DISNEY'S
MICKEY MOUSE
IN "The KLONDIKE KID"
UNITED ARTISTS PICTURE
THIS PAPER LEASED TO THE EXHIBITOR BY UNITED ARTISTS CORPORATION

The Thief of Bagdad
United Artists, 1924

Starring: Douglas Fairbanks
Price: $54,625
Sold: November 2005
Description: One sheet (27" x 41"), Very Fine+ on linen

Fairbanks soars above the city in one of the greatest fantasy films ever made. With help from a magic rope and magic carpet, Fairbanks—who had already starred as Zorro and Robin Hood—further established himself as the first and greatest of film swashbucklers. This poster, featuring bright colors and well-preserved paper, is believed to be the finest specimen in existence.

- The Flying Carpet -

Douglas Fairbanks

The THIEF of BAGDAD

TOP THREE SHEET

The Pride of the Clan
Artcraft, 1917

Starring: Mary Pickford
Price: $53,775
Sold: November 2007
Description: Three sheet (41" x 81"), Fine/Very Fine on linen

By 1917, Pickford was one of the biggest stars in Hollywood, on her way to becoming a show business legend. In *The Pride of the Clan*, she plays a Scottish lass who becomes clan leader after her father dies in a shipwreck. This stone lithograph three sheet is the only one of its kind known to exist. Two years after this movie's release, the "girl with the curls" would launch her own studio, United Artists, with Charlie Chaplin, Douglas Fairbanks, and D.W. Griffith.

MARY PICKFORD

IN

`THE PRIDE OF THE CLAN`

THE SWEETEST STORY EVER SCREENED

DIRECTED BY MAURICE TOURNEUR

PRESENTED BY ARTCRAFT PICTURES CORPORATION

The Raven
Universal, 1935

Starring: Boris Karloff, Bela Lugosi
Price: $50,787.50
Sold: March 2007
Description: Half sheet (22" x 28"), style B, Very Fine

Considered a true gem of horror collecting, this half sheet is one of four specimens known to exist. After the success of 1934's *The Black Cat*, Universal Pictures wasted no time in pairing up Karloff and Lugosi once again for another Edgar Allan Poe adaptation. Although the plot borrowed nothing from the poem except its title, the film was loaded with all sorts of depravity that would have made Poe proud. The colors on this half sheet are bold and vibrant, appearing as fresh as the day it was printed. See also the posters ranked 70 and 90 (shown below).

CARL LAEMMLE presents

KARLOFF
AND
Bela (DRACULA) LUGOSI

IN AN ADAPTATION OF
EDGAR ALLAN POE'S

"The RAVEN"

with
IRENE WARE
LESTER MATTHEWS
INEZ COURTNEY
DIRECTED BY LOUIS FRIEDLANDER
ASSOCIATE PRODUCER DAVID DIAMOND

A UNIVERSAL PICTURE

THE CAST

BELA LUGOSI	as	DR. VOLLIN	KARLOFF	as	BATEMAN	SPENCER CHARTERS	as	COL. GRANT
IRENE WARE	as	JEAN THATCHER	SAMUEL HINDS	as	JUDGE THATCHER	MAIDEL TURNER	as	HARRIET
			INEZ COURTNEY	as	MARY			
LESTER MATTHEWS	as	JERRY HALDEN	IAN WOLFE	as	GEOFFREY	ARTHUR HOYT	as	CHAPMAN

Copyrighted 1935 UNIVERSAL PICTURES CORPORATION Country of Origin U.S.A.

Mad Love
MGM, 1935

Starring: Peter Lorre, Colin Clive
Price: $50,787.50
Sold: March 2009
Description: Title lobby card (11" x 14"), Fine/Very Fine

This film marked the American film debut of Lorre, who would go on to appear in *The Maltese Falcon, Arsenic and Old Lace,* and *Casablanca.* While it received mixed reviews and was unsuccessful at the box office, its reputation as an influential piece of moviemaking has grown in the years since, with some arguing that its visual style influenced *Citizen Kane.* Paper on this title is extremely scarce, with this evocative title lobby card the only one known to exist.

MAD LOVE

Starring

PETER LORRE

WITH

FRANCES DRAKE · **COLIN CLIVE**
TED HEALY and **ISABEL JEWELL**

From the novel "LES MAINS D'ORLAC" by MAURICE RENARD
Directed by KARL FREUND   Produced by JOHN W. CONSIDINE Jr.

A
Metro-Goldwyn-Mayer
PICTURE

"COUNTRY OF ORIGIN U.S.A."

The Hunchback of Notre Dame
Universal, 1929 rerelease

Starring: Lon Chaney
Price: $50,787.50
Sold: March 2009
Description: One sheet (27" x 41"), Very Fine

For decades—until Disney's 1996 animated film—Universal's silent *Hunchback of Notre Dame* was the most famous adaptation of Victor Hugo's classic novel. It remains one of the top-grossing silent films of all time. Originally released in 1923, the film remained so popular that the studio kept the movie in constant rerelease, with most original posters most likely reused by theater owners until their condition made them no longer usable. This stone lithograph poster from a 1929 reissue of the film is the only "Festival of Fools" style of one sheet known to exist.

CARL LAEMMLE presents

THE HUNCHBACK OF NOTRE DAME

WITH LON CHANEY

AND A BRILLIANT CAST

VICTOR HUGO'S
IMMORTAL CLASSIC
A WALLACE WORSELEY Production
IT'S A UNIVERSAL

The Whoopee Party
United Artists, 1932

Starring: Mickey Mouse
Price: $48,300
Sold: October 2002
Description: One sheet (27" x 41"), Very Fine on linen

In 1932, Walt Disney changed distributors of his cartoon shorts from Columbia Studios to United Artists, who were willing to advance more money for the production of his cartoons. While Columbia's Disney posters were two-color, the 13 posters United Artists did for Disney used a full-color process. This dramatic blue and yellow starburst image was among United Artists' first for Disney.

JOSEPH M.SCHENCK
presents
WALT DISNEY'S
MICKEY MOUSE

in "The WHOOPEE PARTY"
UNITED ARTISTS PICTURE

Grand Hotel
MGM, 1932

Starring: Greta Garbo, John Barrymore, Joan Crawford, Wallace Beery,
Lionel Barrymore
Price: $48,000
Sold: July 2006
Description: One sheet (27" x 41"), Fine/Very Fine on linen

MGM took a financial risk by placing all its stars in the same movie. And it paid off handsomely. *Grand Hotel* won the Academy Award® for Best Picture and in the process helped launch the "all-star cast" movie genre. This rare style of one sheet is legendary among poster collectors, with this particular example believed to be in the best condition of those in existence.

Citizen Kane
RKO, 1941

Starring: Orson Welles, Joseph Cotten
Price: $47,800
Sold: March 2009
Description: One sheet (27" x 41"), style B, Very Fine+ on linen

The first feature film directed by Orson Welles is today considered an American classic. This style B one sheet is a wonderful alternative to the artwork featured in most of the film's original campaign, with a painting by William Rose showing Welles, Dorothy Comingore, and Ruth Warrick. This poster sold the film as a more conventional love story, and it's considered by far the more desirable style for the original American release of the film. See also the poster ranked 42 (shown below).

EVERYBODY'S TALKING ABOUT IT!

It's Terrific!

ORSON WELLES

CITIZEN KANE

The Mercury Actors

JOSEPH COTTEN
DOROTHY COMINGORE

EVERETT SLOANE
RAY COLLINS
GEORGE COULOURIS
AGNES MOOREHEAD
PAUL STEWART
RUTH WARRICK
ERSKINE SANFORD
WILLIAM ALLAND

RKO RADIO PICTURES

Babe Comes Home
First National, 1927

Starring: Babe Ruth
Price: $47,800
Sold: April 2009
Description: One sheet (27" x 41"), Very Fine+ on linen

At the height of his fame, Babe Ruth went to Hollywood once again (his first film was 1920's *Headin' Home*) to star in this 60-minute silent romantic comedy, playing Babe Dugan, star of the Los Angeles Angels. This one sheet was made the year Ruth set his home-run record, so the film's producers made sure Ruth was featured prominently. Only two specimens of this one sheet are known to exist.

Love Before Breakfast
Universal, 1936

Starring: Carole Lombard
Price: $47,800
Sold: March 2008
Description: One sheet (27" x 41"), Very Fine/Near Mint

By 1936, Lombard was at the top of her game. With comedies such as *Twentieth Century, My Man Godfrey,* and *Nothing Sacred,* she was a leading lady of the screwball comedy genre. *Love Before Breakfast,* in which she's punched by a romantic interest, is not among her most memorable performances, but this image gains significant cultural value by its appearance in the 1936 print *Houses and Billboards in Atlanta* by renowned photographer Walker Evans, who documented the Great Depression.

CARL LAEMMLE *presents*

Carole Lombard

Faith Baldwin's

LOVE BEFORE BREAKFAST

With PRESTON FOSTER

CESAR ROMERO · JANET BEECHER

FROM THE NOVEL "SPINSTER DINNER"
DIRECTED BY WALTER LANG · AN EDMUND GRAINGER PROD.

A universal picture

Moon Over Miami
20th Century–Fox, 1941

Starring: Don Ameche, Betty Grable, Robert Cummings
Price: $47,800
Sold: November 2008
Description: Three sheet (41" x 81"), Fine/Very Fine on linen

Noted *Esquire* and *Playboy* pinup artist Alberto Vargas is often credited with creating the Grable image for this poster, but it is believed that Vargas's work appeared only in print ads for this musical. Historians believe this particular image was done by a studio-hired artist emulating Vargas's style. In any case, this large-format poster is a stunner. This three sheet has some fold wear and some tape staining at several of the crossfolds. See also the poster ranked 54 (shown below).

in Technicolor
MOON
OVER
MIAMI
A 20th CENTURY-FOX PICTURE
DON AMECHE
BETTY GRABLE
Robert
CUMMINGS
Charlotte
GREENWOOD
Jack
HALEY
Carole
LANDIS
Cobina
WRIGHT JR.
A
PRODUCED BY
HARRY JOE BROWN
DIRECTED BY
Walter Lang
SCREEN PLAY BY VINCENT LAWRENCE AND BROWN HOLMES — ADAPTATION BY GEORGE SEATON AND LYNN STARLING
FROM A PLAY BY STEPHEN POWYS — LYRICS AND MUSIC BY LEO ROBIN AND RALPH RAINGER

The Bride of Frankenstein
Universal, 1935

Starring: Boris Karloff, Colin Clive, Elsa Lanchester
Price: $46,000
Sold: November 2004
Description: Title lobby card (11" x 14"), Very Fine

One of the best specimens known for this legendary title lobby card, featuring images of the Frankenstein monster and his "bride." A relic of the film's impact on audiences is the "SUITABLE ONLY FOR ADULTS" stamp at the bottom, apparently added by a concerned theater owner. A slight bleed from another stamped card can be seen at the top of the card over the line "The Monster Demands a Mate!" See also the posters ranked 1 and 17 (shown below).

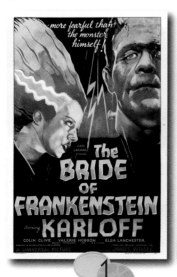

TOP LOBBY CARD

Dracula

Universal, 1931

Starring: Bela Lugosi
Price: $44,812
Sold: March 2008
Description: Lobby card (11" x 14"), Very Fine/Near Mint

This card is considered the best scene in the lobby card set and features Lugosi moving in on the innocent Helen Chandler to feed on her blood. This card is extremely rare, surfacing less frequently than the title card. See also the posters ranked 2, 18, and 59 (shown below).

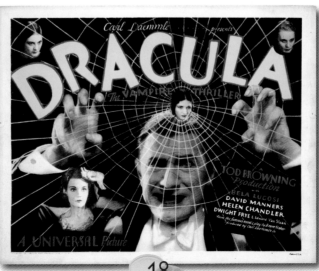

CARL LAEMMLE *presents*

DRACULA

UNIVERSAL PICTURE

COUNTRY OF ORIGIN AND PRODUCTION U.S.A.

Made in U.S.A.

Mickey's Nightmare
United Artists, 1932

Starring: Mickey Mouse
Price: $44,812.50
Sold: March 2009
Description: One sheet (27" x 41"), Fine/Very Fine on linen

Among United Artists' "Magical 13" Mickey Mouse posters, *Mickey's Nightmare* was the first to be released. A plus for collectors: Mickey appears nine times. Three specimens of this poster are known to exist, with this being the best-quality version.

Joseph M. Schenck
presents
WALT DISNEY'S
MICKEY MOUSE
MICKEY'S NIGHTMARE
UNITED ARTISTS PICTURE
THIS PAPER LEASED TO THE EXHIBITOR BY UNITED ARTISTS CORPORATION

The Black Cat

Universal, 1934

Starring: Boris Karloff, Bela Lugosi
Price: $43,700
Sold: July 2002
Description: Half sheet (22" x 28"), style B, Very Fine

This is the only known style B half sheet. No restoration has been performed, and the poster is virtually flawless other than a clean two-inch tear in the AR of KARLOFF. See also the posters ranked 3 and 10 (shown below).

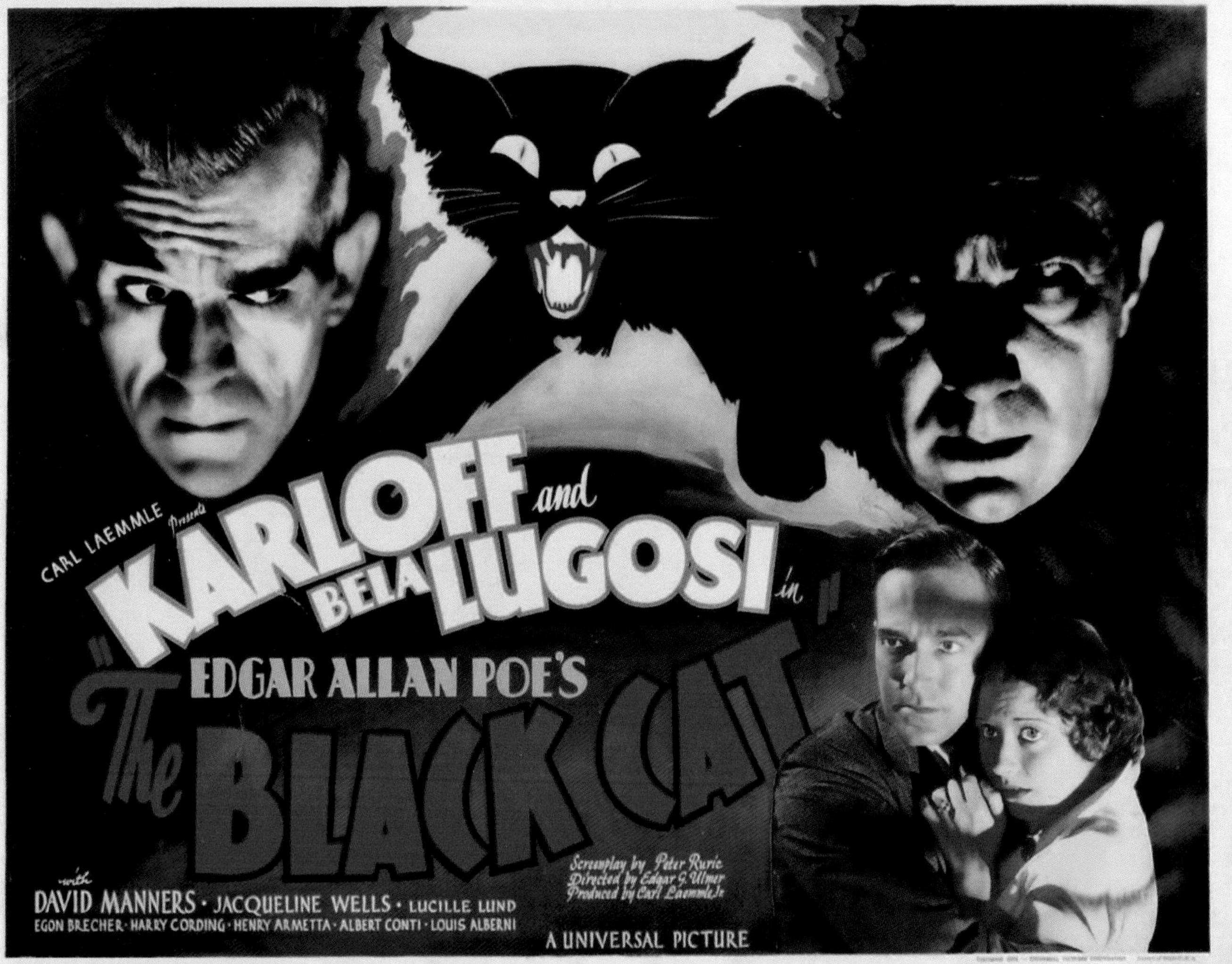

TOP FOREIGN POSTER

Londres Despues de Media Noche (London After Midnight)

MGM, 1927

Starring: Lon Chaney
Price: $41,825
Sold: March 2009
Description: Argentinean poster (29" x 43"), Very Fine–

London After Midnight is one of Hollywood's great "lost" movies, with the only known print of this silent-era classic destroyed in an MGM studio fire in the 1960s. Only a handful of lobby cards and half sheets are known to exist. When this Argentinean poster surfaced for auction, it was the first large paper seen for the film, in which Chaney has dual roles, as both a Scotland Yard detective and, in disguise, a hideous vampire-like character. See also the poster ranked 55 (shown below).

METRO-GOLDWYN-MAYER

PRESENTA A

LON CHANEY

EN

LONDRES DESPUES DE MEDIA NOCHE

(LONDON AFTER MIDNIGHT)

CON MARCELINE DAY y CONRAD NAGEL

DIRECCION DE TOD BROWNING

Escenario de
WALDEMAR YOUNG

La Signora di Shanghai (The Lady From Shanghai)

Columbia, 1947

Starring: Rita Hayworth, Orson Welles
Price: $41,825
Sold: March 2008
Description: Italian four-folio (55" x 78"), Very Fine– on linen

Italian artist Anselmo Ballester created a masterpiece with the artwork for the Italian release of this movie. The film—in which a sailor (Welles) accompanies a beautiful woman (Hayworth) on a cruise and becomes involved in a murder plot—is considered one of the greatest film noirs ever made. According to Hollywood lore, Columbia Pictures president Harry Cohn offered $1,000 to anyone who could explain the convoluted plot to him—something even director Welles reportedly couldn't do.

The War of the Worlds
Paramount, 1953

Starring: Gene Barry, Ann Robinson
Price: $39,435
Sold: November 2006
Description: Half sheet (22" x 28"), style B, Very Fine+

Producer George Pal's classic adaptation of H.G. Wells's science fiction novel is considered one of the top science fiction films of all time. Most of the images used on original-release posters do not depict the Martian warships as seen on this half sheet. This poster has only minor edge wear, two 1" edge tears on the bottom border, and light fold lines.

Citizen Kane
RKO, 1941

Starring: Orson Welles, Joseph Cotten
Price: $39,100
Sold: October 2002
Description: Three sheet (41" x 81"), Very Fine on linen

This three sheet is one of only a few known to have survived. It's certainly the only known specimen actually signed by director Welles (the scribble is visible by Kane's right foot). The signature was obtained in the 1970s by the poster's previous owner, the noted photographer Steve Schapiro. See also the poster ranked 31 (shown below).

The Meller Drammer
United Artists, 1933

Starring: Mickey Mouse
Price: $38,837.50
Sold: November 2006
Description: One sheet (27" x 41"), Very Fine+ on linen

One of United Artists' "Magical 13" Disney posters, this is considered among the most beautiful. This one sheet depicts a scene from the budget-challenged rendition of *Uncle Tom's Cabin* performed by Mickey, Minnie, and Goofy. This poster is the only known example.

JOSEPH M. SCHENCK
▫ PRESENTS ▫
WALT DISNEY'S
MICKEY MOUSE

"THE MELLER DRAMMER"
▫ □ ○ ○ □ ▫
UNITED ARTISTS
PICTURE
□ ○ ○ □

TOP WINDOW CARD

Metropolis
UFA-Paramount, 1927

Starring: Alfred Abel, Brigitte Helm
Price: $38,837.50
Sold: March 2007
Description: Window card (14" x 22"), Fine+ on paper

Director Fritz Lang's futuristic dystopia is considered a silent-era classic. When it appeared at auction in 2007, this window card—distributed for display around town, rather than at theaters—was the only type known. It depicts Helm as Maria in the pivotal transformation scene, in which the inventor Rotwang gives her likeness to his robot. There are minor creases and a light scratch in the top imprint area, some very slight abrasions in the image, and a small tear in Helm's cheek.

The Wolf Man
Universal, 1941

Starring: Lon Chaney Jr., Claude Rains, Bela Lugosi
Price: $38,837.50
Sold: November 2006
Description: Insert (14" x 36"), Very Good on paper

At the beginning of World War II, Universal was working to revive the horror genre, which had kept the studio solvent through the Great Depression. The studio had released *Werewolf of London* five years earlier, but decided to revisit that character with a more horrific story. *The Wolf Man* is now considered one of Universal's greatest horror films. This version is considered the best poster for this classic film, with only a handful known to exist. See also the posters ranked 85 and 86 (shown below).

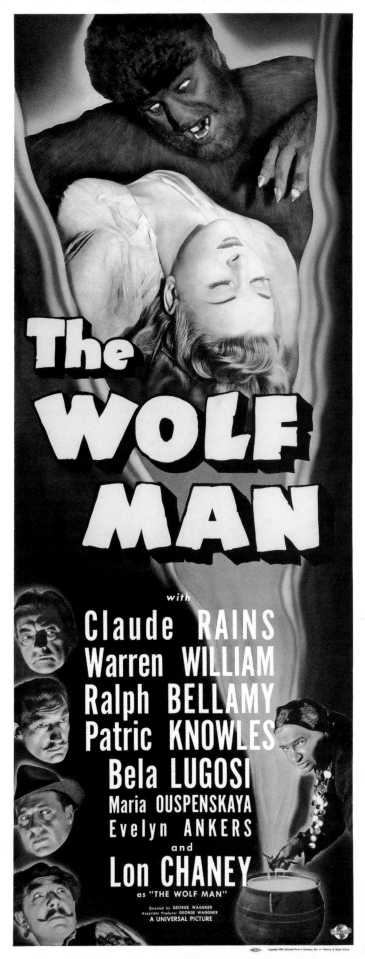

Casablanca
Warner Bros., 1942

Starring: Humphrey Bogart, Ingrid Berman, Paul Henreid,
Claude Rains, Peter Lorre
Price: $38,837.50
Sold: November 2008
Description: Half sheet (22" x 28"), style B, Fine/Very Fine

Against the war-torn backdrop of Casablanca, Bogart and Bergman re-
kindle a romance amid political intrigue, corruption, and murder. It's an
American classic, winning Oscars® for Best Picture, Director, and Screenplay. This style B half sheet is among the rarest and most desirable of all
Casablanca posters. Unlike style A, it shows not only Bogart and Bergman
but all of the main characters. See also the posters ranked 80, 83, and 92
(shown below).

HUMPHREY BOGART · INGRID BERGMAN · PAUL HENREID

Presented by
WARNER BROS.

A HAL B. WALLIS
PRODUCTION

"Casablanca"

CLAUDE CONRAD SYDNEY PETER
RAINS VEIDT GREENSTREET LORRE

Directed by MICHAEL CURTIZ

SCREEN PLAY BY JULIUS J. & PHILIP G. EPSTEIN AND HOWARD KOCH
FROM A PLAY BY MURRAY BURNETT AND JOAN ALISON · MUSIC BY M. STEINER
A WARNER BROS. — FIRST NATIONAL PICTURE

The Eagle
United Artists, 1925

Starring: Rudolph Valentino
Price: $38,837.50
Sold: July 2007
Description: One sheet (27" x 41"), Very Fine/Near Mint on linen

---

Valentino was the screen's first male sex symbol, and *The Eagle*—a romantic adventure made to capitalize on the popularity of the Douglas Fairbanks blockbuster *The Mark of Zorro*—is considered one of his finest films. The silent movie, based on a story by Alexander Pushkin, was the first under Valentino's United Artists contract. He made only one other—*Son of the Sheik*—before his untimely death in 1926.

John W. Considine, Jr.
presents

RUDOLPH
VALENTINO
in "THE EAGLE"

SUPPORTED BY
VILMA BANKY AND LOUISE DRESSER
screen story by Hans Kraly
A CLARENCE BROWN PRODUCTION
A United Artists Picture

Frankenstein
Universal, 1938 rerelease

Starring: Boris Karloff, Colin Clive
Price: $38,837.50
Sold: November 2008
Description: Three sheet (41" x 81"), Very Fine+ on linen

Unlike today, movie studios often rereleased movies as long as fans would line up. This three sheet for the 1938 rerelease of *Frankenstein* is done in a style reminiscent of German Expressionism. To date, this is the only known three sheet from any *Frankenstein* release. Once belonging to actor Nicolas Cage, this example is amazingly clean with only slight repair to a minor crease in the chest area of the monster. Like many three sheets from the mid-1930s on, this example was printed in two parts, and a flaw is visible where the two sections do not quite align (notice, for example, the right vertical edge near the windmill). Many two-part three sheets of the era feature this kind of flaw. See also the posters ranked 5 and 60 (shown below).

King Kong
RKO, 1933

Starring: Fay Wray, Robert Armstrong
Price: $36,800
Sold: March 2002
Description: One sheet (27 " x 41 "), style B, Very Good

While the style A version shows the giant ape atop the Empire State Building, style B has a less vicious-looking Kong rampaging through the streets. See the style A poster ranked 13 (shown below).

KING KONG
with
FAY WRAY....
ROBERT ARMSTRONG
BRUCE CABOT
A COOPER-SCHOEDSACK
PRODUCTION
RKO
Radio
PICTURES
FROM AN IDEA CONCEIVED BY
EDGAR WALLACE
AND MERIAN C. COOPER

TOP SIX SHEET

The Grapes of Wrath
20th Century–Fox, 1940

Starring: Henry Fonda
Price: $35,850
Sold: July 2007
Description: Six sheet (81" x 81"), Very Fine on linen

Director John Ford's film of John Steinbeck's harrowing novel, with its leftist political overtones, was toned down for audiences of 1940. But the movie, which often shows up on lists of great American films, remains a powerful depiction of the Great Depression and its devastating effects. This six sheet features a stark title graphic and artwork by Thomas Hart Benton, who in the early 1930s created murals for public buildings throughout the Midwest. A rare instance in which the work of a great American artist is used to promote a film.

DARRYL F. ZANUCK'S Production of

THE GRAPES OF WRATH

BY John Steinbeck

Benton

WITH Henry **FONDA** AND *Jane* DARWELL *John* CARRADINE
Charley GRAPEWIN *Dorris* BOWDON
Russell SIMPSON O.Z. WHITEHEAD *John* QUALEN *Eddie* QUILLAN *Zeffie* TILBURY
Directed by **JOHN FORD** A 20th CENTURY·FOX PICTURE
Associate Producer and Screen Play by Nunnally Johnson

It Happened One Night
Columbia, 1934

Starring: Clark Gable, Claudette Colbert
Price: $35,850
Sold: March 2008
Description: Three sheet (41" x 81"), style B, Very Fine– on linen

The first film to sweep the five major Oscars®: Best Actor, Best Actress, Best Picture, Best Director, and Best Screenplay. Two of the big screen's leading stars were cast in this story about a spoiled heiress who runs away from her father and new husband and falls in love with a reporter looking for a great story. The film is among the last romantic comedies released before the Motion Picture Association of America began enforcing its Production Code. This stone lithograph is the only known of its kind.

Another Fine Mess
MGM, 1930

Starring: Stan Laurel, Oliver Hardy
Price: $35,850
Sold: November 2006
Description: One sheet (27" x 41"), Very Fine+

Of Laurel and Hardy's 40 short sound films, the title for *Another Fine Mess*—in which they play tramps being chased by police—is based on Hardy's famous catchphrase (which actually was "Another nice mess"). It's also a remake of their silent comedy *Duck Soup,* in which they first shared top billing. This poster, with artwork by caricature artist Al Hirschfeld, is the only one known to exist.

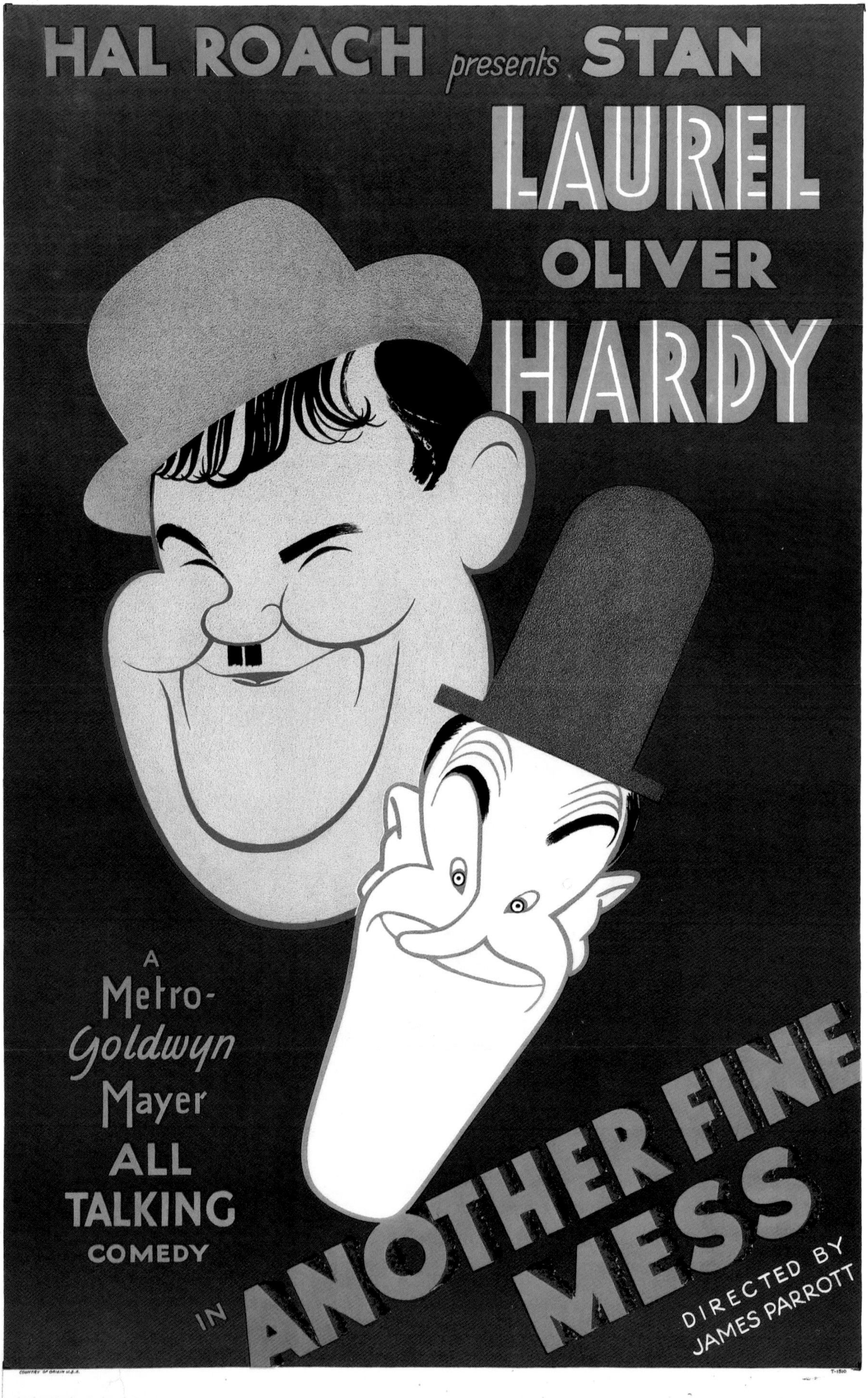
HAL ROACH presents STAN
LAUREL
OLIVER
HARDY
A
Metro-
Goldwyn
Mayer
ALL
TALKING
COMEDY
IN
ANOTHER FINE
MESS
DIRECTED BY
JAMES PARROTT
COUNTRY OF ORIGIN U.S.A.
T-1510

The Rescue
United Artists, 1929

Starring: Ronald Colman, Lily Damita
Price: $35,850
Sold: March 2008
Description: One sheet (27" x 41"), Fine/Very Fine on linen

The 1926 silent film *Beau Geste* established English actor Ronald Colman as a "Valentino type" swashbuckler. A year after this movie was released, Colman achieved critical success when his performances in both *Condemned* and *Bulldog Drummond* received Best Actor Oscar® nominations. This romantic adventure, based on Joseph Conrad's novel, follows an adventurer who helps hide a prince and his sister on the run from rebellious natives.

Samuel Goldwyn
presents
RONALD
COLMAN
in "The Rescue"
by JOSEPH CONRAD
with Lily Damita
A
HERBERT BRENON
-PRODUCTION-
UNITED
ARTISTS
PICTURE

Moon Over Miami
20th Century–Fox, 1941

Starring: Don Ameche, Betty Grable, Robert Cummings
Price: $35,850
Sold: March 2008
Description: One sheet (27" x 41"), style B, Fine/Very Fine on linen

Grable, on her way to being the highest-paid star in the movies, graces this extremely elusive style B one sheet. At the height of American pinup culture, Grable notoriously had her legs insured for a million dollars. "There's a reason I'm successful in show business," she once said, "and I'm standing on both of them." See also the poster ranked 34 (shown below).

Londres Après Minuit (London After Midnight)

MGM, 1927

Starring: Lon Chaney
Price: $35,850
Sold: March 2008
Description: Prewar Belgian poster (24.5" x 33.5"), Very Fine on linen

This dramatic stone lithograph Belgian poster, with the Loew-Metro-Goldwyn logo in the upper right, has fold wear with slight crossfold separation and pinholes with minor staining in the corners and borders. Professional restoration has addressed these minor flaws. See also the poster ranked 39 (shown below).

The Benson Murder Case
Paramount, 1930

Starring: William Powell
Price: $33,460
Sold: November 2008
Description: Insert (14" x 36"), Very Fine– on paper

Powell stars as S.S. Van Dine's amateur detective Philo Vance in this third installment of the series. The most intriguing aspect of this poster is the stunning art deco image of Powell—reminiscent of the work of Cubist painter Juan Gris. It is unlike any other art used in the campaign. The poster, one of a very few known to exist, has been paper-backed to repair cracked folding, typical of inserts of this age. See also the poster ranked 78 (shown below).

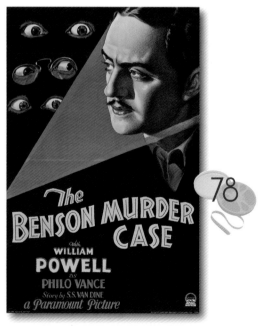

SEE
WILLIAM POWELL AS
PHILO VANCE

unravel the most baffling of all mysteries

THE BENSON MURDER CASE

STORY BY S. S. VAN DINE

A Paramount Picture

Hawaiian Holiday
RKO, 1937

Starring: Mickey Mouse
Price: $33,460
Sold: March 2009
Description: Poster (30" x 40"), Very Fine on paper

In one of the first Disney shorts distributed by RKO, Mickey takes the gang to Hawaii, serenading Minnie while Pluto chases crabs and Goofy learns to surf. This 30" x 40" size is among the rarest for any Disney poster, with this *Hawaiian Holiday* specimen the only one known to exist.

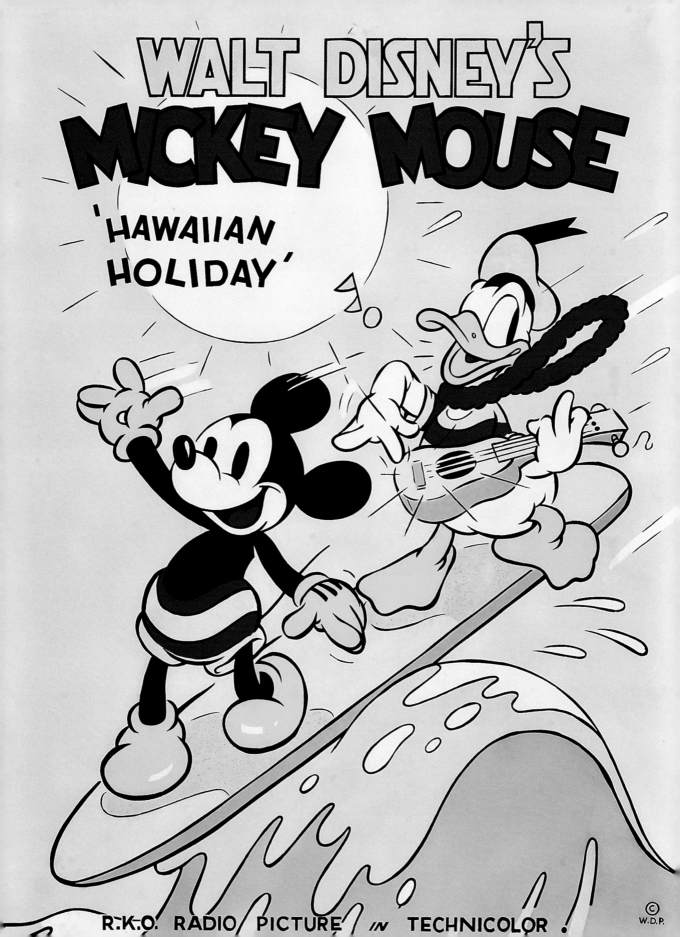

Gilda
Columbia, 1946

Starring: Rita Hayworth, Glenn Ford
Price: $33,460
Sold: July 2009
Description: One sheet (27" x 41"), style B, Fine+ on linen

Hayworth tore up the screen in her signature role as the ultimate femme fatale in this intricate noir classic, which includes Ford at his best. One of the most iconic and desirable posters of the film noir genre, this style B one sheet is extremely hard to come by. Restoration has addressed most issues, including a small chip in the upper left corner.

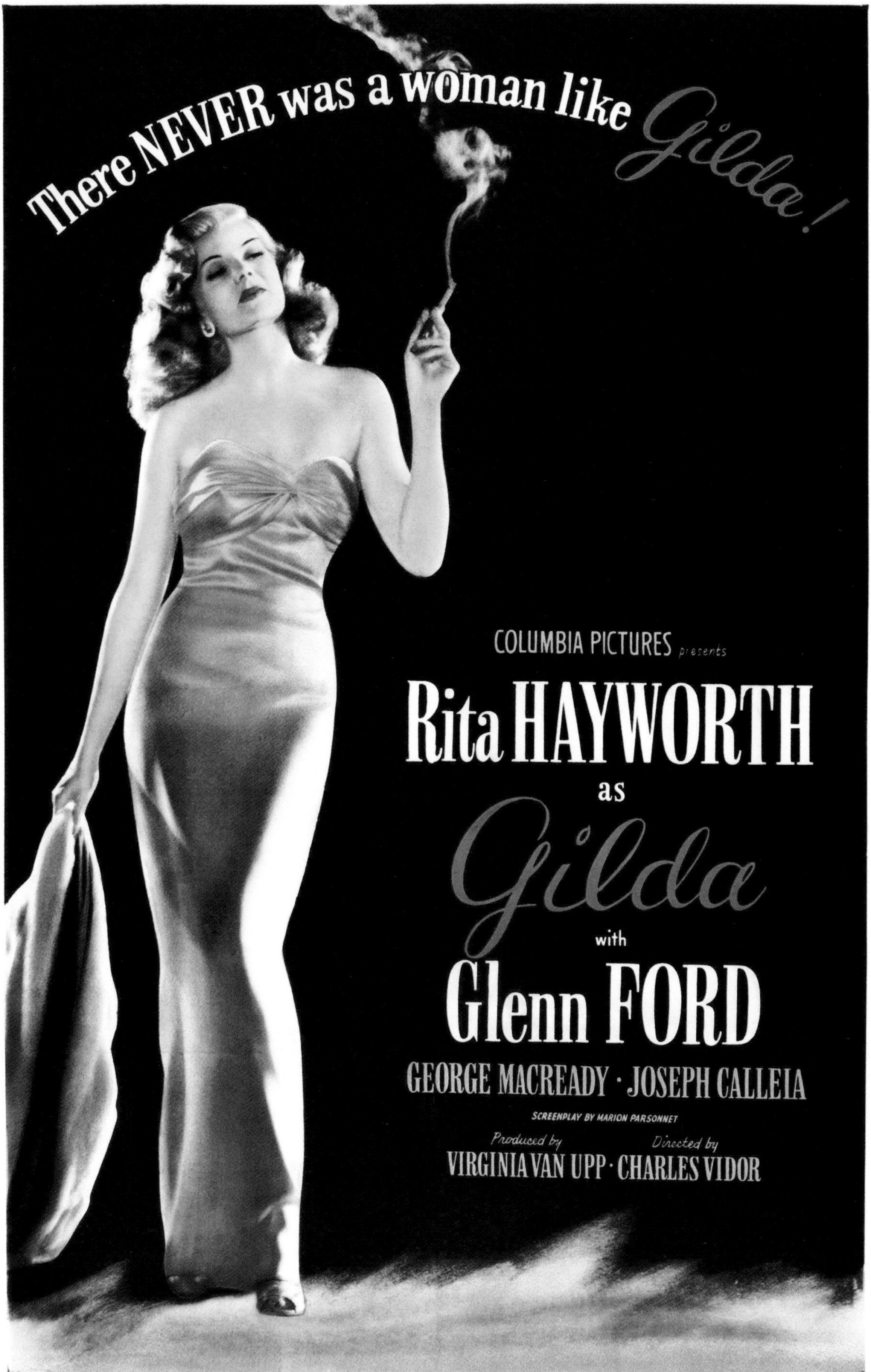
There NEVER was a woman like Gilda!
COLUMBIA PICTURES presents
Rita HAYWORTH
as
Gilda
with
Glenn FORD
GEORGE MACREADY · JOSEPH CALLEIA
SCREENPLAY BY MARION PARSONNET
Produced by
VIRGINIA VAN UPP
Directed by
CHARLES VIDOR
Country of Origin U.S.A.
46/559

Dracula

Universal, 1938 rerelease

Starring: Bela Lugosi
Price: $33,460
Sold: November 2008
Description: One sheet (27" x 41"), Fine+ on linen

Seven years after its original release, Universal sent its classic back to theaters. Perhaps as a gimmick, some of the film's prints were given a green tint. The one sheet used for this "new look" release—similar to the original style A one sheet issued in 1931—was printed with dark green and black ink, capturing Lugosi in his most menacing pose. This specimen was found in Pennsylvania in 2003, eventually finding its way into the collection of actor Nicolas Cage. At the time of its sale, no other examples of this one sheet had surfaced. See also the posters ranked 2, 18, and 36 (shown below).

DRACULA

WITH

**BÉLA LUGOSI · DAVID MANNERS
HELEN CHANDLER · DWIGHT FRYE**
and **EDWARD VAN SLOAN**

A TOD BROWNING PRODUCTION
from the famous Novel & Play by BRAM STOKER
PRODUCED BY
A UNIVERSAL PICTURE · CARL LAEMMLE JR.

Frankenstein

Universal, 1931

Starring: Boris Karloff, Colin Clive
Price: $33,460
Sold: March 2007
Description: Title lobby card (11" x 14"), Very Fine

At least 10 examples of this title card are known, but rarely do they have colors as vivid and bold as this example. The card shows some light foxing along the left border and some minor creasing in the lower corners. There were two pinholes in the lower right corner, three in the lower left corner, four in the upper left corner, and six in the upper right corner. All have been repaired. See also the posters ranked 5 and 48 (shown below).

Scarface
United Artists, 1932

Starring: Paul Muni, Ann Dvorak, Boris Karloff
Price: $33,460
Sold: November 2007
Description: One sheet (27" x 41"), Fine+ on linen

With eccentric millionaire Howard Hughes producing and the influential Howard Hawks directing, this is one of the most bullet-riddled, violent, and important gangster films ever made. Al Pacino starred in the equally influential 1983 remake. Censors wanted Hughes's original title changed and recommended "The Shame of the Nation." After a compromise, the film was released with the title *Scarface, the Shame of a Nation.* Two versions of the title appear on surviving posters and lobby cards: *Scarface,* and *Scarface* with "The Shame of a Nation" overprinted on existing paper. It appears this one sheet escaped the "Shame of a Nation" overprint, with some speculating it is from one of Hughes's personal distributions of the film while he was trying to get it passed by various censors.

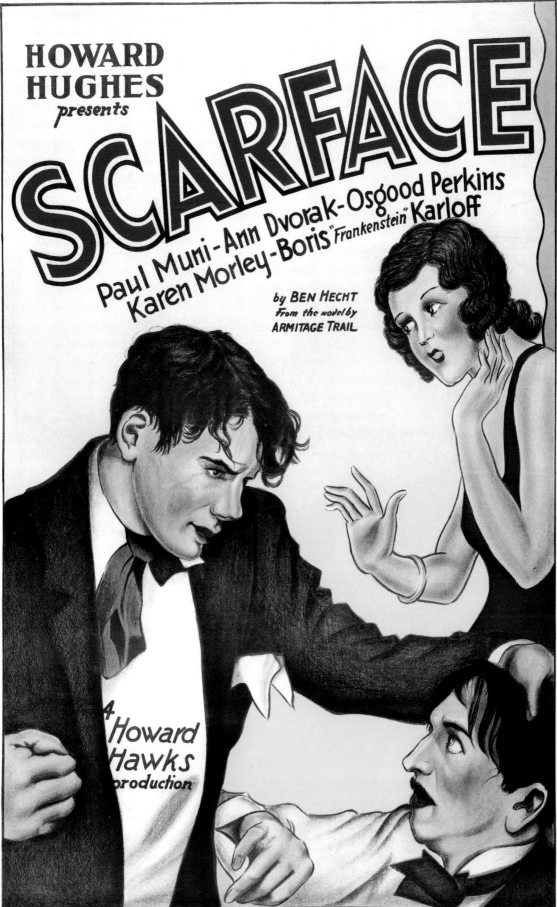

Magician Mickey
United Artists, 1937

Starring: Mickey Mouse
Price: $33,460
Sold: July 2007
Description: Poster (40" x 60"), Fine/Very Fine on linen

One of the best Mickey Mouse cartoons from Disney's Golden Age, full of fast-paced animation and absolutely hilarious situations. The pyrotechnic sleight of hand at the conclusion, involving stagehand Goofy, makes spectacular use of the still-young Technicolor process. One of the rarest Mickey posters, this specimen has been linen backed to address border wear, small tears, and general handling wear.

Modern Times
United Artists, 1936

Starring: Charlie Chaplin
Price: $33,460
Sold: July 2007
Description: Six sheet (81" x 81"), Fine/Very Fine on linen

Modern Times marked the last appearance of the "Little Tramp." Filmed between 1932 and 1936, it was directed, written, scored, and produced by Chaplin himself. No one ever had as much success blending biting social commentary with pure slapstick. This is a magnificent stone lithograph image of one of the screen's greatest comedians in one of his masterpieces.

CHARLIE *Chaplin*

in

MODERN TIMES

Written, Directed and Produced
by CHARLES CHAPLIN
Released thru United Artists

The Champion
Essanay, 1915

Starring: Charlie Chaplin
Price: $33,460
Sold: March 2009
Description: One sheet (27" x 41"), Very Good+ on paper

Chaplin's third film for Essanay was one of his best as far as plotting, characterization, and humor. Chaplin plays a down-and-out tramp who becomes the gym's champ with help from his lucky horseshoe and faithful bulldog. Edna Purviance costars, with "Broncho Billy" Anderson, a founder of Essanay and the cinema's first major cowboy star, making a cameo appearance. Original posters from this early Chaplin release are scarce, and this style one sheet is one of only two known examples.

CHARLIE CHAPLIN

THE CHAMPION

ESSANAY-CHAPLIN COMEDY

DISTRIBUTED BY GENERAL FILM CO., INC.

ESSANAY
TRADE MARK.
REG. U.S. PAT. OFF.

ESSANAY

GEORGE K. SPOOR, PRESIDENT

Morgan
LITHO CO.
CLEVELAND U.S.A.

Things to Come
United Artists, 1936

Starring: Raymond Massey, Ralph Richardson
Price: $32,862.50
Sold: November 2007
Description: One sheet (27" x 41"), Very Fine

H.G. Wells wrote the screenplay as a loose adaptation of his own 1933 novel *The Shape of Things to Come* and his 1931 nonfiction work *The Work, Wealth and Happiness of Mankind*. Predictions of the world's future, from prescient visions of World War II to wildly imaginative ideas of life in 2035, fill this epic British production. Posters for this early science fiction film have always been scarce, and this beautiful, unrestored one sheet is magnificent.

The Outlaw
United Artists, 1943

Starring: Jane Russell
Price: $32,200
Sold: November 2004
Description: Six sheet (81" x 81"), Very Fine/Near Mint

Like *Scarface* before it, Howard Hughes's *The Outlaw* was controversial even before it was released. When censors saw a rough cut of the film, they labeled it salacious for the number of overt shots of Russell's breasts and cleavage. Hughes was forced to cut 40 minutes from the movie. On February 5, 1943, the film opened at San Francisco's Geary Theatre. People turned out in droves, and Russell, making her motion picture debut, became a national sensation. Provocative posters of Russell were plastered across San Francisco. Some posters, such as this one, advertised that Russell could be seen in person at the theater. Although this claim sounds like mere ballyhoo, it was the truth. Hughes was so incensed at the changes that following each screening he had Russell and costar Jack Beutel perform live a 20-minute scene that had been cut from the film.

The Adventures of Sherlock Holmes
20th Century–Fox, 1939

Starring: Basil Rathbone
Price: $31,070
Sold: March 2007
Description: Six sheet (81" x 81"), Very Fine+

Considered one of the best films of the series, this is the second to feature Rathbone as Arthur Conan Doyle's famed detective. Based on the stage play by William Gillette, it features the oft-repeated line "Elementary, my dear Watson." Until this specimen showed up, no one had ever seen one of these large-size posters. The color is bright and fresh, and the paper supple and white.

The Adventures of
SHERLOCK HOLMES

WITH Basil **RATHBONE** — Nigel **BRUCE**

Ida **LUPINO** — Alan **MARSHAL**

AND Terry **KILBURN** George **ZUCCO** Henry **STEPHENSON** E.E. **CLIVE**

A 20th CENTURY-FOX PICTURE · Darryl F. Zanuck IN CHARGE OF PRODUCTION

DIRECTED BY ALFRED WERKER ASSOCIATE PRODUCER Gene Markey SCREEN PLAY BY EDWIN BLUM & WILLIAM DRAKE

BASED ON THE PLAY "SHERLOCK HOLMES" BY WILLIAM GILLETTE WITH THE PERMISSION OF THE EXECUTORS OF THE LATE SIR ARTHUR CONAN DOYLE

The Adventures of Robin Hood
Warner Bros., 1938

Starring: Errol Flynn, Olivia de Havilland, Basil Rathbone, Claude Rains
Price: $31,070
Sold: March 2007
Description: Six sheet (81" x 81"), Fine/Very Fine on linen

At the time of its sale, this was the only known six sheet for one of Hollywood's greatest swashbuckler adventures. The climactic sword fight between Rathbone and Flynn is dramatically and wonderfully represented here. Minor defects have been expertly restored. See also the posters ranked 94 and 96 (shown below).

The Broadway Melody
MGM, 1929

Starring: Charles King, Anita Page, Bessie Love
Price: $31,070
Sold: July 2009
Description: One sheet (27" x 41"), Fine/Very Fine on linen

This poster represents a film with numerous firsts. It was MGM's first musical. It was Hollywood's first all-talking musical. It was the first sound film to win an Academy Award® for Best Picture. It was among the first musicals to feature a Technicolor sequence (though today this is presumed lost). The classic song "Give My Regards to Broadway" was also given its debut in the film. It was the biggest Hollywood sensation of the decade and spawned a series of Broadway-themed blockbusters for MGM.

The Raven

Universal, 1935

Starring: Boris Karloff, Bela Lugosi
Price: $29,875
Sold: March 2009
Description: One sheet (27" x 41"), style D, Very Good/Fine on linen

Prior to restoration, the poster had about one quarter of an inch trimmed from around the border and two two-inch crossfold tears in Karloff's mouth. All defects have been restored so that the poster now displays beautifully. It is one of only two known specimens. See also the posters ranked 26 and 90 (shown below).

CARL LAEMMLE presents
KARLOFF
AND
Bela (DRACULA) LUGOSI
IN AN ADAPTATION OF
EDGAR ALLAN POE'S
"The RAVEN"
with
IRENE WARE
LESTER MATTHEWS
INEZ COURTNEY
DIRECTED BY LOUIS FRIEDLANDER
ASSOCIATE PRODUCER DAVID DIAMOND
A UNIVERSAL PICTURE

Son of Frankenstein

Universal, 1939

Starring: Basil Rathbone, Boris Karloff, Bela Lugosi
Price: $28,680
Sold: March 2008
Description: Title lobby card (11" x 14"), Very Fine–

This hard-to-find title lobby card features Rathbone as the son of the famed doctor and Lugosi as Ygor, the demented hunchback. There is creasing on the bottom border with a corner bend on the left, pinholes in the top two corners, one crease in the top border, and some light soiling on the white borders. See also the poster ranked 9 (shown below).

BASIL **RATHBONE** · BORIS **KARLOFF** · BELA **LUGOSI**

in **SON of FRANKENSTEIN**

with **Lionel ATWILL** · **Josephine HUTCHINSON**

DONNIE DUNAGAN · **EMMA DUNN** · **EDGAR NORTON**

The Cocoanuts
Paramount, 1929

Starring: The Marx Brothers
Price: $28,680
Sold: July 2007
Description: Insert (14" x 36"), Very Good on paper

Straight from their hit Broadway show, *The Cocoanuts* marks Groucho, Chico, Harpo, and Zeppo's big-screen debut. The movie also includes the first appearance of Margaret Dumont in a Marx Brothers film. She would go on to appear in almost all of the brothers' later comedies. This is the only known specimen. See also the poster ranked 89 (shown below).

Paramount's **ALL TALKING** *Musicomedy Hit*

THE
MARX BROTHERS

with **OSCAR**
SHAW
AND
MARY
EATON

IN

THE COCOANUTS

MUSIC AND LYRICS BY
IRVING BERLIN
BOOK BY GEORGE S. KAUFMAN
DIRECTED BY JOSEPH SANTLEY
AND ROBERT FLOREY
ADAPTED BY MORRIE RYSKIND

2953 *COUNTRY OF ORIGIN U.S.A.*

Mickey's Pal Pluto
United Artists, 1933

Starring: Mickey Mouse
Price: $28,680
Sold: November 2006
Description: One sheet (27" x 41"), Very Fine on linen

One of United Artists' "Magical 13," this stone lithograph one sheet puts earlier Columbia duotone and later RKO posters to shame. In this animated short, Pluto rescues some kittens, but then feels rejected when the cute furballs seem to get better treatment from Mickey and Minnie.

Violent Is the Word for Curly
Columbia, 1938

Starring: The Three Stooges
Price: $28,680
Sold: July 2007
Description: One sheet (27" x 41"), Fine on linen

In a spoof of the 1936 film *Valiant Is the Word for Carrie*, Larry, Curly, and Moe pose as professors at Mildew College. The film features "Swinging the Alphabet," the only full-length song performed by the Stooges in their nearly 200 short films. This is one of the most desirable of the early Columbia Stooges posters, featuring a central image of the trio and two scenes from the film.

THEY'RE CRACKED IN THE CRANIUM...ON A CUCKOO CAMPUS!

THE 3 STOOGES

MOE, LARRY and CURLY

VIOLENT IS THE WORD *for* CURLY

with Eddie Fetherston • Marjorie Dean • Gladys Gale
Directed by Charley Chase
Produced by Charley Chase and Hugh McCollum

A COLUMBIA 2-REEL COMEDY

Duck Soup

Paramount, 1933

Starring: The Marx Brothers
Price: $28,680
Sold: November 2006
Description: Half sheet (22" x 28"), style B, Fine– on paper

Groucho as Rufus T. Firefly is named dictator of Freedonia and promptly goes to war with his neighbor, Sylvania. The film is the last Marx Brothers movie to feature Zeppo, and the last of Paramount's five Marx Brothers releases. It is widely considered a Marx Brothers masterpiece. This is the only known style B half sheet. The poster has been paper backed and expertly restored.

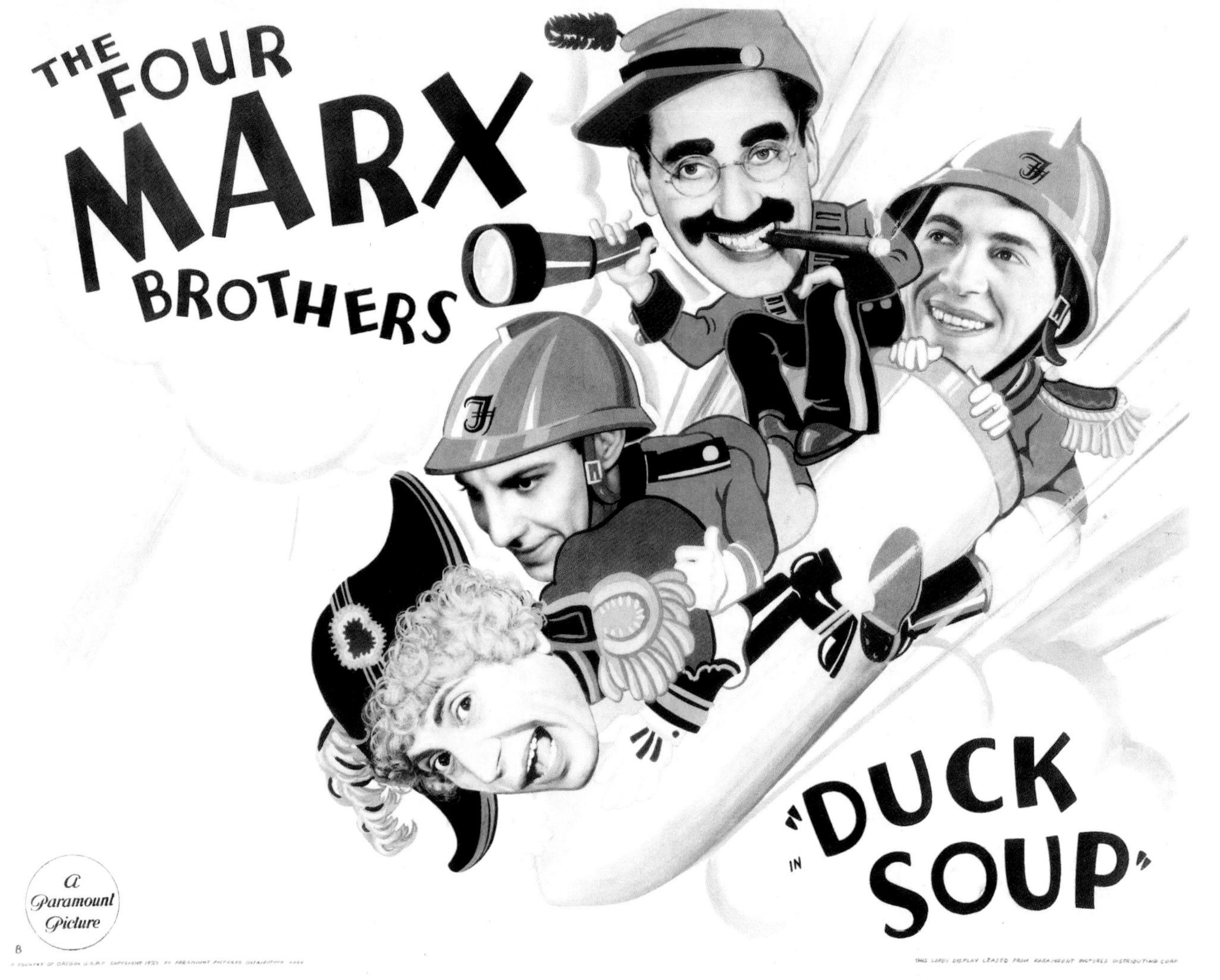
THE FOUR
MARX
BROTHERS
IN
"DUCK
SOUP"
A Paramount Picture
B

The Black Pirate
United Artists, 1926

Starring: Douglas Fairbanks
Price: $27,600
Sold: March 2006
Description: One sheet (27" x 41"), Fine/Very Fine on linen

Fairbanks's superb acrobatic skills were on full display in this classic silent epic, which was among the first movies to be shot in the two-strip Technicolor process. Many critics place the film among the actor's best work, and this poster is among the most sought-after one sheets of the silent era.

Douglas Fairbanks
AS
"The Black Pirate"

Photographed by Technicolor Process

M
Nero-Film AG, 1931

Starring: Peter Lorre
Price: $26,290
Sold: November 2006
Description: German poster (37" x 83"), Fine on linen

Based on the real-life case of child-killer Peter Kuerten, the "monster of Dusseldorf," this film, directed by Fritz Lang, was Lorre's first major starring role. *M* has been called an early German sound film masterpiece. Although *The Maltese Falcon* (1941) is traditionally credited as the first film noir, there is little doubt that *M* anticipated many essential features of the genre.

The Benson Murder Case

Paramount, 1930

Starring: William Powell
Price: $26,290
Sold: March 2009
Description: One sheet (27" x 41"), Very Fine+ on linen

This stone lithograph full-bleed one sheet is the only known specimen of this beautifully designed poster. Unlike the larger insert, this poster includes a clear image of Powell. Restoration and linen backing have been expertly done. See also the poster ranked 56 (shown below).

The BENSON MURDER CASE

with

WILLIAM POWELL

as

PHILO VANCE

Story by S.S. VAN DINE

a Paramount Picture

TOP MIDGET WINDOW CARD

Flying Down to Rio
RKO, 1933

Starring: Dolores Del Rio, Ginger Rogers, Fred Astaire
Price: $26,290
Sold: July 2008
Description: Midget window card (8" x 14"), Very Fine/Near Mint

Window cards were typically printed on card stock for display away from theaters, including venues such as barbershops, bakeries, and even telephone poles. The only defect on this mini version of the one sheet is a single pinhole in the top display area. See also the posters ranked 4 and 81 (shown below).

A MUSICAL EXTRAVAGANZA STAGED IN THE CLOUDS
ROMANCE THAT SOARS TO THE SKIES ON THE WINGS OF SONG
FLYING DOWN TO RIO
with DOLORES DEL RIO
GENE RAYMOND • RAUL ROULIEN
GINGER ROGERS • FRED ASTAIRE
MUSIC BY VINCENT YOUMANS
DIRECTED BY THORNTON FREELAND
MERIAN C. COOPER – Executive Producer
LOUIS BROCK – Associate Producer
LYRICS BY EDWARD ELISCU AND GUS KAHN
RKO Radio Pictures
COUNTRY OF ORIGIN U. S. A.

Casablanca
Warner Bros., 1953 rerelease

Starring: Humphrey Bogart, Ingrid Bergman, Paul Henreid,
Claude Rains, Peter Lorre
Price: $26,290
Sold: November 2006
Description: Italian two-folio (39" x 55"), Very Fine

Italian movie fans had to wait until after World War II to see this classic wartime love story. Bogart and Bergman are stunning in this illustration by Italian poster artist Luigi Martinati. This poster was done for the third rerelease of the movie in Italy. See also the posters ranked 46, 83, and 92 (shown below).

Top Two Sheet

Flying Down to Rio
RKO, 1933

Starring: Dolores Del Rio, Ginger Rogers, Fred Astaire
Price: $26,290
Sold: July 2008
Description: Two sheet (41" x 54"), Fine/Very Fine on linen

This extremely rare two sheet was printed only for distribution in the New York area and used for outdoor advertising. It is the only known surviving example, having been saved by the original artist, Harold Seroy, and passed down to his family. Seroy started in the Warner Bros. art department in 1930 and went on to work for all the major studios until retiring in 1960. See also the posters ranked 4 and 79 (shown below).

STUPENDOUS MUSICAL!
200 BEAUTIES!
HAROLD SEROY
FLYING DOWN TO RIO
with
DOLORES DEL RIO
GENE RAYMOND
GINGER ROGERS
FRED ASTAIRE
T.J. HAYES PRINT CO., N.Y.

The Wayward Canary
United Artists, 1932

Starring: Mickey Mouse
Price: $26,290
Sold: March 2007
Description: One sheet (27" x 41"), Very Fine+ on linen

This is among the first of United Artists' "Magical 13" Mickey Mouse posters. It was released the same year that the Academy awarded Disney a special Oscar® for his creation of a nationwide phenomenon. This stone lithograph one sheet has only minimal fold-line touch-up.

COLLECTIBLE MOVIE POSTERS

Casablanca

Warner Bros., 1942

Starring: Humphrey Bogart, Ingrid Bergman, Paul Henreid,
Claude Rains, Peter Lorre
Price: $25,300
Sold: March 2005
Description: One sheet (27" x 41"), Very Fine+ on linen

The studio originally wanted George Raft, Ronald Reagan, and Ann Sheridan
for the cast, but director Michael Curtiz demanded Bogart and Bergman. He
was right, as Bogart went on to receive an Oscar® nomination for Best Actor.
Of the *Casablanca* one sheets, this is considered one of the best-designed. See
also the posters ranked 46, 80, and 92 (shown below).

Creature From the Black Lagoon

Universal International, 1954

Starring: Julia Adams, Richard Carlson
Price: $25,095
Sold: July 2008
Description: One sheet (27" x 41"), Near Mint/Mint

One of the greatest monster films of all time, this was Universal's reentry into the genre, a horror film for the post-atomic age of the 1950s. The result is a masterpiece. Discovered during a scientific expedition to the Amazon, the Gill Man proved popular enough to star in several sequels. This highly desirable one sheet is as clean as they come, unbacked and unrestored.

CREATURE
from the
Black LAGOON

Starring
RICHARD CARLSON · JULIA ADAMS

with RICHARD DENNING · ANTONIO MORENO · NESTOR PAIVA · WHIT BISSELL

DIRECTED BY JACK ARNOLD · SCREENPLAY BY HARRY ESSEX AND ARTHUR ROSS · PRODUCED BY WILLIAM ALLAND · A UNIVERSAL-INTERNATIONAL PICTURE

45771   54/109

The Wolf Man
Universal, 1941

Starring: Lon Chaney Jr., Claude Rains, Bela Lugosi
Price: $24,150
Sold: March 2003
Description: One sheet (27" x 41"), Very Fine+ on linen

"Even a man who is pure in heart and says his prayers by night," a character utters in this classic film, "may become a wolf when the wolf bane blooms, and the autumn moon is bright." This was the last of the great Universal horror monsters to be introduced in the 1940s, and the film is still one of the most atmospheric of the studio's output. See also the posters ranked 45 and 86 (shown below).

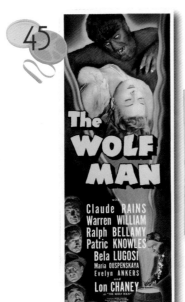

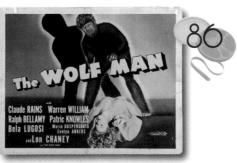

THE WOLF MAN

with

CLAUDE RAINS
WARREN WILLIAM
RALPH BELLAMY
PATRIC KNOWLES
BELA LUGOSI
MARIA OUSPENSKAYA
EVELYN ANKERS

and

LON CHANEY

as "The Wolf Man"

Directed by GEORGE WAGGNER   A UNIVERSAL PICTURE   Associate Producer GEORGE WAGGNER

The Wolf Man
Universal, 1941

Starring: Lon Chaney Jr., Claude Rains, Bela Lugosi
Price: $23,900
Sold: November 2006
Description: Half sheet (22" x 28"), Very Good/Fine on paper

Under Jack Pierce's incredible makeup, Chaney became the screen's greatest werewolf—featured here towering over his victim. Although title lobby cards and one sheets have turned up over the years, this half sheet is rare. See also the posters ranked 45 and 85 (shown below).

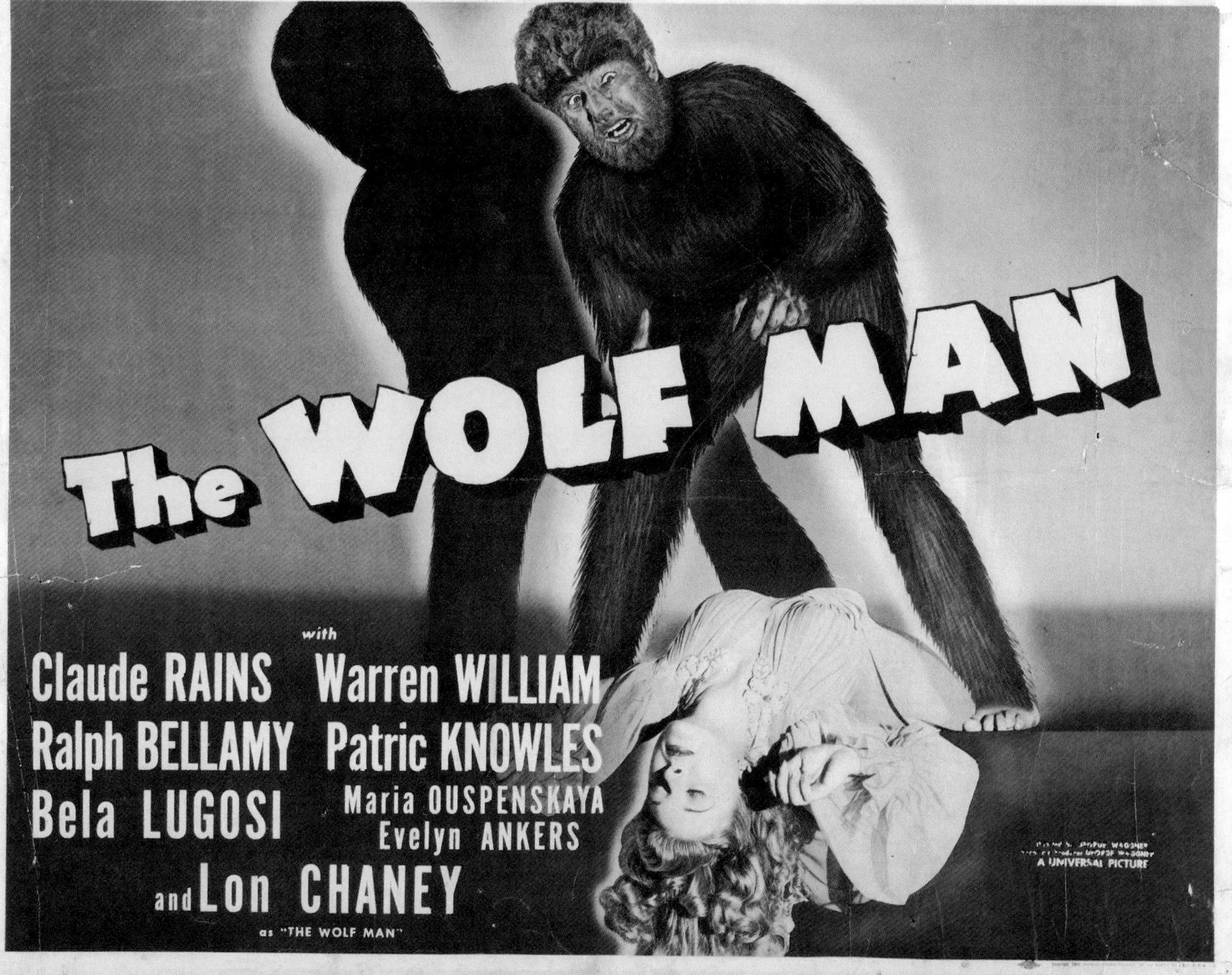

THE WOLF MAN

with

Claude RAINS   **Warren WILLIAM**

Ralph BELLAMY   **Patric KNOWLES**

Bela LUGOSI   Maria OUSPENSKAYA
Evelyn ANKERS

and **Lon CHANEY**
as "THE WOLF MAN"

A UNIVERSAL PICTURE

Gold Diggers of 1933
Warner Bros., 1933

Starring: Dick Powell, Ginger Rogers
Price: $23,900
Sold: November 2007
Description: One sheet (27" x 41"), style B, Very Fine+ on linen

---

Based on the 1919 Broadway play by Avery Hopwood, this is the story of a young man (Powell) who bankrolls a struggling Broadway show and finds true love in the process. This movie introduced the songs "We're in the Money," "Remember My Forgotten Man," and "Pettin' in the Park" (a notoriously pre-Code number). This ultra-rare style B version is one of only a handful known to exist, and features stunning artwork of Powell, Rogers, Joan Blondell, Ruby Keeler, and Guy Kibbee.

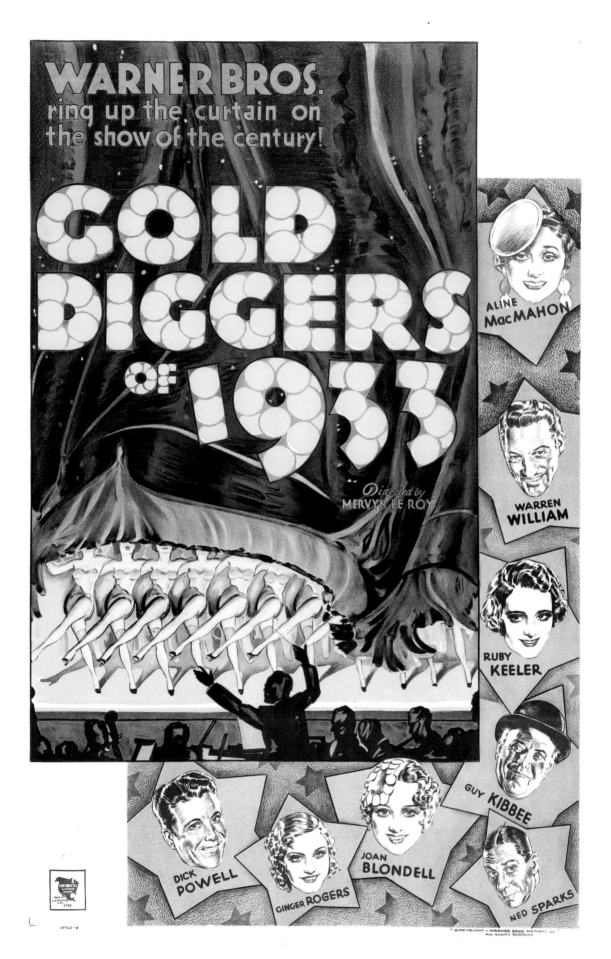

Faust
MGM-UFA, 1926

Starring: Gosta Ekman, Emil Jannings
Price: $23,900
Sold: November 2008
Description: One sheet (27" x 41"), Fine/Very Fine

F.W. Murnau was a cinematic genius. Best known as the director of *Nosferatu* (1922), he also filmed an early version of *Dr. Jekyll and Mr. Hyde* (1920) and the brilliant character study *Der Letzte Mann* (1924; released in the United States under the title *The Last Laugh*). In his adaptation of the Faust legend, Ekman stars as the aged seeker of knowledge and pleasure who turns to dark forces to satisfy his longings. Murnau's film is one of horror's most visually stunning cinematic nightmares, an archetypal tale of love, power, morality, temptation, and redemption. This unrestored stone lithograph one sheet from the U.S. release of the film is the only known specimen.

GOETHE'S
FAUST
Directed by F.W. Murnau with
EMIL JANNINGS
An
UFA
Production
J.H. TOOKER
PRINT CO.
DISTRIBUTED BY
Metro-Goldwyn-Mayer
COUNTRY OF ORIGIN & PRODUCTION, U.S.A.

The Cocoanuts

Paramount, 1929

Starring: The Marx Brothers
Price: $23,900
Sold: March 2008
Description: Lobby card (11" x 14"), Very Fine–

Lobby cards for *The Cocoanuts* in which the Marx Brothers are pictured are as rare as they come. This beautiful card, with a deco design and image of Groucho, Chico, and Zeppo, is an extraordinary find. Professional restoration has addressed a tear in the bottom right corner, light edge wear, and several pinholes in the border. See also the poster ranked 72 (shown below).

The Raven

Universal, 1935

Starring: Boris Karloff, Bela Lugosi
Price: $23,900
Sold: November 2007
Description: Title lobby card (11" x 14"), Very Good/Fine

This title card is one of a handful known to exist and is among the most sought-after in the pantheon of horror collecting. Interestingly, the facial images of Karloff and Lugosi mirror the images used for the half sheets of *The Black Cat,* which was released the previous year and also starred the two men. See also the posters ranked 26 and 70 (shown below).

CARL LAEMMLE
presents
KARLOFF and
Bela (DRACULA) LUGOSI
IN AN ADAPTATION OF EDGAR ALLAN POE'S
"The RAVEN"
with
IRENE WARE
LESTER MATTHEWS
INEZ COURTNEY
DIRECTED BY LOUIS FRIEDLANDER
ASSOCIATE PRODUCER DAVID DIAMOND
A UNIVERSAL PICTURE

Mickey Mouse Stock Poster
United Artists, 1932–1933

Starring: Mickey Mouse
Price: $23,900
Sold: November 2007
Description: One sheet (27" x 41"), Fine/Very Fine

This stock sheet is probably the first sheet to be distributed by United Artists when the studio took over distribution in 1932. This incredibly rare poster, featuring Mickey in his iconic pose, is seldom seen in a grade good enough to stand alone without restoration. Bright, vibrant colors highlight this unrestored beauty.

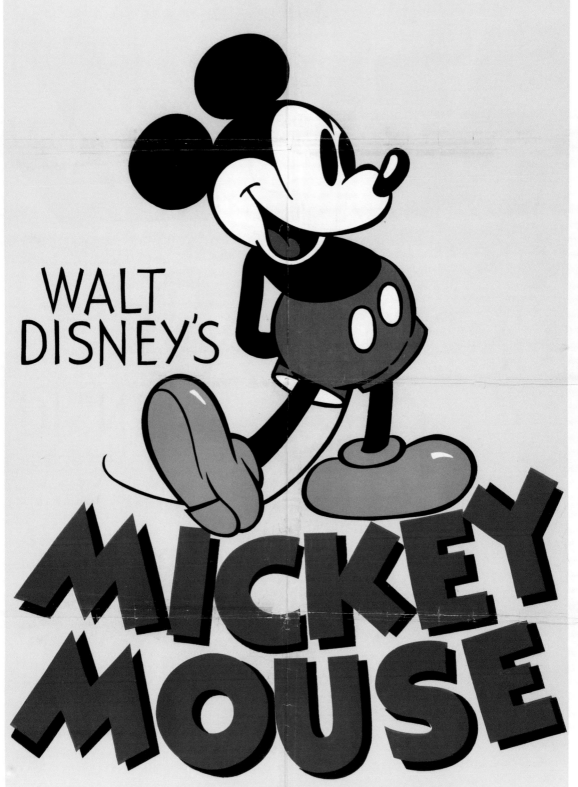

WALT DISNEY'S

MICKEY MOUSE

Released *thru* UNITED ARTISTS

Tooker · Moore Lithograph Co., Inc.   136 W. 52nd St., New York

Printed in U. S. A.

Casablanca
Warner Bros., 1942

Starring: Humphrey Bogart, Ingrid Bergman, Paul Henreid,
Claude Rains, Peter Lorre
Price: $23,000
Sold: March 2006
Description: Half sheet (22" x 28"), style A, Very Fine+

During World War II, Warner Bros. produced most of its posters in two colors to conserve expenses. For *Casablanca*, posters were printed in tones of red and black. For this stunning half sheet, the studio went full color with Bogart and Bergman in a cheek-to-cheek embrace. This style half sheet is identical to the title card and is one of the most important and popular movie posters ever produced. Only one other example has surfaced in the past 20 years. See also the posters ranked 46, 80, and 83 (shown below).

HUMPHREY **BOGART** · INGRID **BERGMAN** · PAUL **HENREID**

Presented by
WARNER BROS.

"*Casablanca*"

CLAUDE **RAINS** · CONRAD **VEIDT** · SYDNEY **GREENSTREET** · PETER **LORRE**

A HAL B. WALLIS PRODUCTION

Directed by **MICHAEL CURTIZ**

SCREEN PLAY BY JULIUS J. & PHILIP G. EPSTEIN and HOWARD KOCH · FROM A PLAY BY MURRAY BURNETT and JOAN ALISON
MUSIC BY MAX STEINER · A WARNER BROS. — FIRST NATIONAL PICTURE

Country of Origin U.S.A

The Phantom of the Opera
Universal, 1925

Starring: Lon Chaney, Norman Kerry, Mary Philbin
Price: $23,000
Sold: November 2004
Description: Insert (14" x 36"), Fine on paper

This ultra-scarce poster for Universal's horror classic features the vengeful composer who lives in the catacombs beneath the Paris Opera House. Surface creases, tears, border chips, small holes, and some paper loss in the upper left corner have been addressed with professional restoration. See also the poster ranked 6 (shown below).

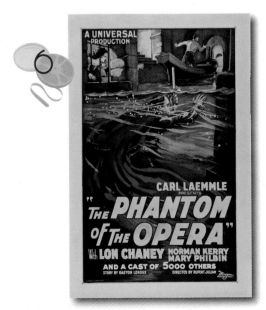

The Adventures of Robin Hood
Warner Bros., 1938

Starring: Errol Flynn, Olivia de Havilland, Basil Rathbone, Claude Rains
Price: $22,705
Sold: November 2006
Description: Three sheet (41" x 81"), Very Fine+ on linen

Warner Bros. originally wanted James Cagney in the title role, until he quit the studio. Flynn stepped in and performed the role with such relish that he created the standard for all future Robin Hoods. Flynn strikes his most romantic pose in this rare three sheet—clutching Maid Marian on his rearing horse. It's believed there are no more than four specimens extant in this format. See also the posters ranked 68 and 96 (shown below).

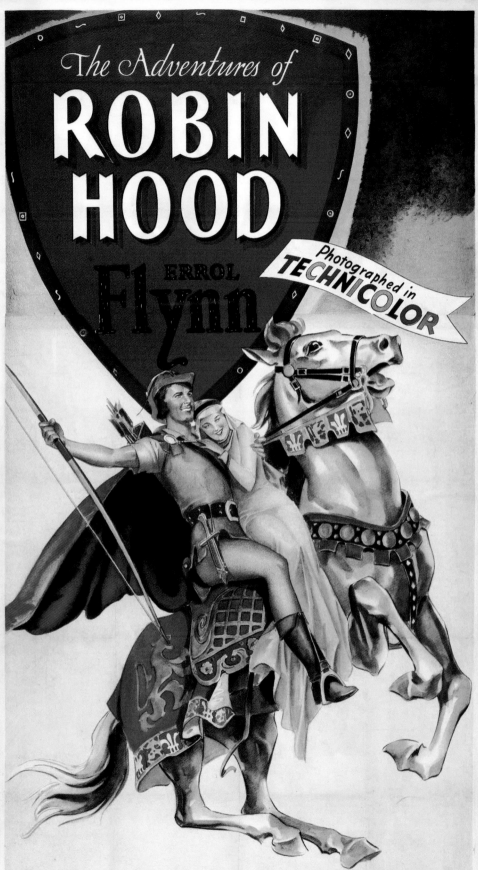

This Gun for Hire
Paramount, 1942

Starring: Veronica Lake, Robert Preston, Alan Ladd
Price: $22,705
Sold: July 2008
Description: One sheet (27" x 41"), Very Fine

Although he received fourth billing as a hit man bent on revenge, this movie was Alan Ladd's breakout performance. It was also the first pairing of Ladd and Lake, a duo that would become icons of film noir. The one sheet is considered one of the best graphically designed posters of the entire hobby. Several examples of this poster have surfaced in recent years, with this sale of the best-condition example being the most recent.

VERONICA
LAKE · ROBERT
PRESTON

THIS GUN
FOR HIRE

WITH
LAIRD CREGAR · ALAN LADD

Screen Play by Albert Maltz and W. R. Burnett · · · · Based on the Novel by Graham Greene
DIRECTED BY FRANK TUTTLE · · · · · A PARAMOUNT PICTURE

The Adventures of Robin Hood
Warner Bros., 1938

Starring: Errol Flynn, Olivia de Havilland, Basil Rathbone, Claude Rains
Price: $22,107.50
Sold: November 2007
Description: One sheet (27" x 41"), Fine+ on linen

This classic poster, with its dynamic image of Robin, is bold and striking. This poster was originally folded, as most posters of this era were, and there are some pinholes in the corners, but professional linen backing has made these flaws invisible. The colors are bright and powerful. See also the posters ranked 68 and 94 (shown below).

Godzilla
Toho, 1954

Price: $21,850
Sold: July 2005
Description: Japanese B2 poster (20" x 28.5"), Very Fine+

In 1954, Toho Studios introduced what would become the longest-running film series in history. More than 25 films have featured the "King of the Monsters." A heavily edited version of this film hit American screens three years later, with additional footage featuring Raymond Burr. With its antiwar, antinuclear message, producers believed the original version would have been out of sync with the Cold War vibe of mid-'50s America.

Attack of the 50 Foot Woman
Allied Artists, 1958

Starring: Allison Hayes
Price: $21,510
Sold: July 2007
Description: Three sheet (41" x 81"), Fine+ on linen

Hell hath no fury like a 50-foot woman scorned. Hayes plays Nancy Archer, who encounters an alien, grows to giant size, and then proceeds to seek revenge against her philandering husband. The movie, often called one of the worst science fiction films ever made, has been spoofed and parodied countless times. No six sheet was produced for this film, making this the largest poster available for this movie.

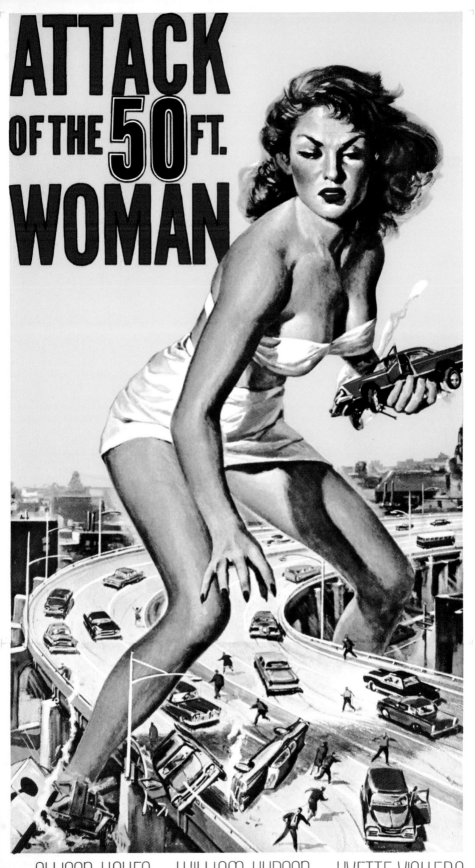

The Oregon Trail
Republic, 1936

Starring: John Wayne
Price: $21,510
Sold: November 2008
Description: One sheet (27" x 41"), Very Fine– on linen

Three years before his breakthrough role in *Stagecoach*, Wayne starred in this "horse opera" about a U.S. Army captain in search of his missing father. While not the most notable Wayne film, its poster is considered among Wayne's best. Republic rarely issued stone lithographs for their B westerns, but they pulled out all the stops for this beauty. Experts believe fewer than six specimens exist.

Lonesome Ghosts
RKO, 1937

Starring: Mickey Mouse
Price: $21,510
Sold: July 2009
Description: Poster (30" x 40"), Very Fine on paper

Nearly 50 years before *Ghostbusters*, Mickey Mouse, Donald Duck, and Goofy were "Ajax Ghost Exterminators" on the hunt for ghosts. This gem is one of the rare silkscreen posters Disney produced for two years beginning in 1937. The process allows for a heavier ink application, which results in a richer, more colorful image. This poster has been paper backed with minimal restoration.

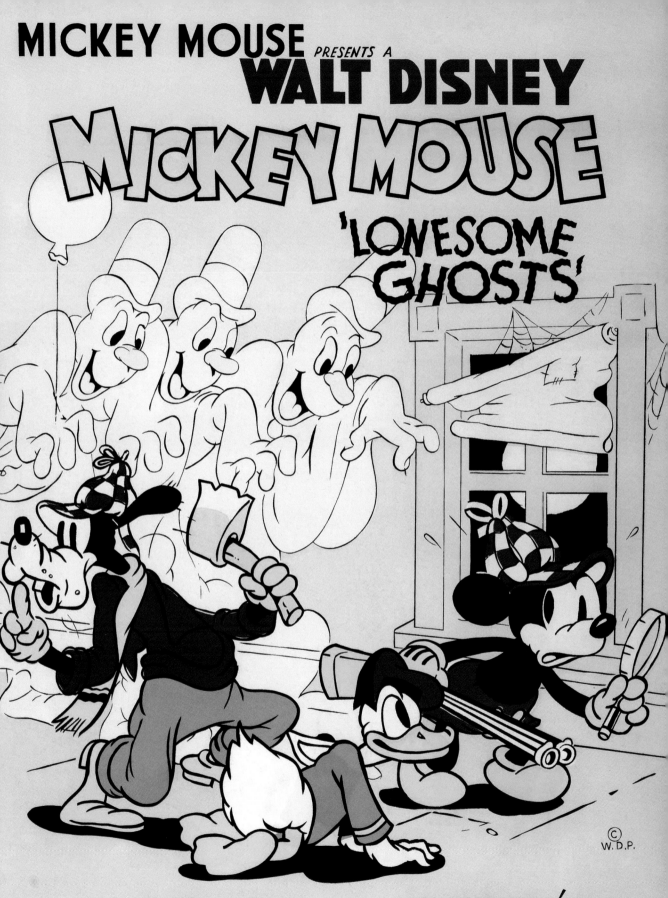

APPENDIX A
MOST POPULAR STARS

The following stars are represented by at least three posters in the 100 ranked in this book.

★ 15 ★
Boris Karloff

★ 15 ★
Bela Lugosi

★ 12 ★
Mickey Mouse

★ 10 ★
Claude Rains

★ 7 ★
Colin Clive

★ 6 ★
Peter Lorre

★ 6 ★
Basil Rathbone

★ 5 ★
Lon Chaney

★ 4 ★
Ingrid Bergman

★4★
Humphrey Bogart

★4★
Paul Henreid

★4★
Ginger Rogers

★3★
Robert Armstrong

★3★
Fred Astaire

★3★
Lon Chaney Jr.

★3★
Olivia de Havilland

★3★
Dolores Del Rio

★3★
Errol Flynn

★3★
Elsa Lanchester

★3★
Marx Brothers

★3★
Orson Welles

APPENDIX B
RELEASES BY YEAR

The following chart gives the number of ranked posters for each year spanned by this collection, from 1915 to 1958.

YEAR	NUMBER	YEAR	NUMBER	YEAR	NUMBER	YEAR	NUMBER
1915	1	1926	2	1937	4	1948	0
1916	0	1927	6	1938	6	1949	0
1917	1	1928	0	1939	4	1950	0
1918	0	1929	5	1940	1	1951	0
1919	0	1930	3	1941	7	1952	0
1920	0	1931	6	1942	4	1953	2
1921	0	1932	8	1943	1	1954	2
1922	0	1933	13	1944	0	1955	0
1923	1	1934	4	1945	0	1956	0
1924	1	1935	8	1946	1	1957	0
1925	3	1936	4	1947	1	1958	1

APPENDIX C
NUMBER OF POSTERS BY STUDIO

STUDIO	POSTERS
Universal	27
United Artists	19
RKO	11
Paramount	11
Warner Bros.	9
MGM	8
20th Century-Fox	4
Columbia	4
Other (1 each)*	7

* Artcraft, First National, Essanay, Nero-Film AG, Toho, Allied Artists, and Republic.

20th Century-Fox

The studio emerged in 1935 from the merger of Fox Film Corporation and Twentieth Century Pictures. It was led by Darryl F. Zanuck, who would produce some of the studio's most memorable films, including *All About Eve, The Grapes of Wrath,* and *The Longest Day.* Studio stars included Shirley Temple, Betty Grable, Henry Fonda, and Marilyn Monroe. Later studio classics include *Butch Cassidy and the Sundance Kid, Patton,* and *Star Wars.* Its top movie represented here is *Moon Over Miami.*

Columbia

Originally founded in 1920 under the name of C.B.C. Film Sales, Columbia Pictures today is part of the Columbia TriStar Motion Picture Group, owned by Sony Pictures Entertainment. Crucial early talent included director Frank Capra and stars Cary Grant, Rita Hayworth, Glenn Ford, and William Holden. Its top poster in this selection is for the Italian release of *The Lady From Shanghai.*

MGM

MGM (Metro-Goldwyn-Mayer) was founded in 1924 with the merger of three production companies. In the following years, the studio made stars of Lon Chaney, Jean Harlow, Clark Gable, Joan Crawford, and Greta Garbo. Its classic movies include *Ben-Hur, The Big Parade, Tarzan the Ape Man, Grand Hotel, Mutiny on the Bounty,* and *A Night at the Opera.* Its top movie in this selection of posters is the creepy Tod Browning–directed *Freaks.*

Paramount

Founded in 1912, Paramount was among the early leaders of quality films. With *Wings,* the studio in 1929 won the first Academy Award® for Best Picture. It received a string of Best Picture nominations between 1949 and 1955. The studio's top movie in this collection is 1923's *Hollywood.*

RKO

With most of its success during Hollywood's Golden Age, RKO Radio Pictures—formed in 1928—is best known for producing *King Kong* and *Citizen Kane.* In addition to its "B" westerns, RKO also produced musicals starring Fred Astaire and Ginger Rogers. Katharine Hepburn, Robert Mitchum, and Cary Grant also were RKO stars, with the studio leaving an influential mark on the film noir genre. Its top movie in this collection is the musical *Flying Down to Rio.*

United Artists

Founded in 1919 by Hollywood friends Charlie Chaplin, Mary Pickford, Douglas Fairbanks, and director D.W. Griffith, United Artists functioned as a distribution company for independent producers. Partners included Samuel Goldwyn, Howard Hughes, and Walt Disney. By 1950, the company had virtually ceased operations as a production house and distributor. The top United Artists film in this collection is the Disney short *The Mad Doctor.*

Universal

Founded in 1912 by German immigrant Carl Laemmle, Universal was responsible for silent classics such as *The Hunchback of Notre Dame* before practically inventing monster movies in the 1930s. The studio's glow diminished in the 1940s as storylines increasingly focused on horror, lowbrow comedy, and teen culture. It regained its prestige in the 1950s, and later established a high-powered partnership with director Steven Spielberg. Universal created the most posters in this collection (27 out of 100), with its top movie poster in this selection being *The Bride of Frankenstein.*

Warner Bros.

Founded by immigrant brothers in 1918, the company is now part of a massive media empire. Its 1927 release of *The Jazz Singer* starring Al Jolson signaled the beginning of the talking-pictures era. The company acquired a majority interest in First National in 1928. The top Warner Bros. poster on this list is *Baby Face* starring Barbara Stanwyck. First National's top movie in this poster collection is *Babe Comes Home.*

**Like father, like son: Carl Laemmle and his son, Carl Jr.,
created an enduring legacy with their films for Universal Pictures.
Also shown is Carl Jr.'s sister, Rosabelle.**

A glance at the top posters in this collection might leave you wondering: who is Carl Laemmle?

Actually, there were two Carl Laemmles.

The elder Laemmle (1867–1939; pronounced LEM-lee) was a founder of Universal Pictures and responsible for classic silent movies such as *The Hunchback of Notre Dame* (1923) and *The Phantom of the Opera* (1925). By 1929, Carl Laemmle Jr. (1908–1979), at the age of 21, was named production chief at Universal. He picked up where his father left off, and further developed the horror genre.

The younger Laemmle insisted on high-quality—some would say extravagant— films, and promptly went into production with *All Quiet on the Western Front,* based on the classic novel by Erich Maria Remarque. Perhaps more important to film fans, Laemmle also pursued the works of Mary Shelley, Bram Stoker, and H.G. Wells.

"Carl Laemmle Jr. was more creative than his father, and better educated," says film historian Bernard F. Dick, author of *City of Dreams: The Making and Remaking of Universal Pictures* (University Press of Kentucky, 1997). "He understood the classics and dealt with works with a pedigree."

Movie fans were soon horrified—and entertained—by *Frankenstein, Dracula,* and *The Invisible Man.* "The Laemmles saw box office and went for it," says Grey Smith, director of vintage movie posters at Heritage Auction Galleries.

Despite the prominent display of the Laemmle name on these posters, credit also must be given to directors like James Whale *(Bride of Frankenstein, The Invisible Man)* and Tod Browning *(Dracula),* who made many of these Laemmle productions artistic successes. "These are the men," Dick says, "who really visualized those scripts."

After producing some of the most popular movies of Hollywood's Golden Age, the Laemmle era was over by 1936, when father and son were forced out of Universal after numerous big-dollar productions and commercially unsuccessful films in the midst of the Great Depression.

BIBLIOGRAPHY

In addition to the works listed below, resources for the collector include various series of books by authors such as Richard Allen, Bruce Hershenson, and Tony Nourmand and Graham Marsh; and Heritage movie-poster auction catalogs by Grey Smith.

Basinger, Jeanine. *The Star Machine*. Knopf, 2007.

Basten, Fred E. *The Lost Artwork of Hollywood: Classic Images From Cinema's Golden Age*. Watson-Guptill, 1996.

Borde, Raymond, Etienne Chaumeton, and Paul Hammond. *A Panorama of American Film Noir (1941–1953)*. City Lights, 2002.

Dick, Bernard. *City of Dreams: The Making and Remaking of Universal Pictures*. University Press of Kentucky, 1997.

———. *Engulfed: The Death of Paramount Pictures and the Birth of Corporate Hollywood*. University Press of Kentucky, 2001.

Dickos, Andrew. *Street With No Name: A History of the Classic American Film Noir*. University Press of Kentucky, 2002.

Edwards, Dianna. *Picture Show: Classic Movie Posters From the TCM Archives*. Chronicle, 2003.

Gomery, Douglas. *The Hollywood Studio System: A History*. British Film Institute, 2008.

Heide, Robert, and John Gilman. *Starstruck: The Wonderful World of Movie Memorabilia*. Repr. Doubleday, 1986.

Hirshhorn, Clive. *The Universal Story: The Complete History of the Studio and All Its Films*. Hamlyn, 2001.

Jewell, Richard. *The Golden Age of Cinema: Hollywood 1929–1945*. Wiley-Blackwell, 2007.

King, Emily. *A Century of Movie Posters: From Silent to Art House*. Barron's Educational Series, 2003.

Kobel, Peter. *Silent Movies: The Birth of Film and the Triumph of Movie Culture*. Little, Brown, 2007.

Lindsay, Cynthia. *Dear Boris: The Life of William Henry Pratt A.K.A. Boris Karloff*. Limelight Editions, 1995.

Mank, Gregory William. *Bela Lugosi and Boris Karloff: The Expanded Story of a Haunting Collaboration*. McFarland, 2009.

Mordden, Ethan. *The Hollywood Studios*. Knopf, 1988.

Petty, John, and Grey Smith. *Capes, Crooks & Cliffhangers: Heroic Serial Posters of the Golden Age*. Ivy Press, 2009.

Rebello, Stephen. *Reel Art: Great Posters From the Golden Age of the Silver Screen*. Abbeville Press, 1992.

Rhodes, Gary D., and Richard Sheffield. *Bela Lugosi: Dreams and Nightmares*. Collectables Press, 2007.

Rigby, Jonathan. *American Gothic: Sixty Years of Horror Cinema*. Reynolds & Hearn, 2007.

Schatz, Thomas. *The Genius of the System: Hollywood Filmmaking in the Studio Era*. Holt, 1996.

Schickel, Richard. *You Must Remember This: The Warner Bros. Story*. Running Press, 2008.

Stanley, Robert H. *The Celluloid Empire: A History of the American Movie Industry*. Hastings House, 1978.

Vieira, Mark A. *Hollywood Dreams Made Real: Irving Thalberg and the Rise of MGM*. Abrams, 2008.

———. *Hollywood Horror: From Gothic to Cosmic*. Abrams, 2003.

Weaver, Tom, Michael Brunas, and John Brunas. *Universal Horrors: The Studio's Classic Films, 1931–1946*. 2nd ed. McFarland, 2007.

INDEX OF ACTORS

INDEX OF FILM TITLES

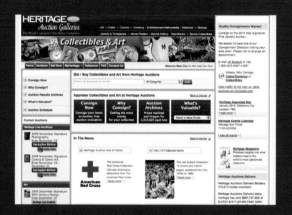